1999

THE
B&B
DIRECTORY OF NEW ZEALAND

winner **TRAVELLERS CHOICE**
best **B&B** of **1998**
as voted by our readers

Colonial Cottage, Auckland.
*'instantly felt welcome', 'wonderful breakfasts', 'attention to detail',
'very clean', 'superior hostess'*

Vote for the Best **B&B 1999** see page 131

Published by The New Zealand B&B Directory Ltd
P O Box 76, Alexandra
New Zealand
Fax: 03 449 2947
Email: greg@holdsworths.co.nz

© The New Zealand B&B Directory Ltd 1998

ISBN: 0-9583704-2-7

Printed by: Spectrum Print Ltd, Christchurch
Design: Tonic Design, Christchurch

All rights reserved, including the right of
reproduction in whole or in part in any form.

Much of the information contained in this directory
has been supplied by the bed and breakfast hosts.
No responsibility is taken by the publishers for errors
and omissions.
Published information is subject to change.

how to use the directory

Abbreviations used in the listings are as follows:

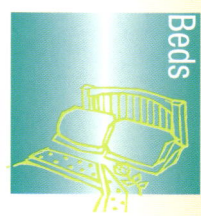

Beds

K = king or super king bed
Q = queen bed
D = double bed
S = single bed

Bathrooms

EN = ensuite - non-share, accessed from within guest room
PR = private - non-share, accessed from outside guest room
GS = guest share - share with other guests
FS = family share - share with other guests and host family

Breakfast

Continental - tea, coffee, juice, toast and cereal
Cooked - continental breakfast plus a cooked portion if required. eg. bacon and eggs
Special - extra-effort breakfast including something different from standard continental or cooked breakfasts, eg. pancakes, eggs benedict

The **tariff** range printed is for one nights accommodation including breakfast (unless otherwise stated) and goods and services tax (GST). Reduced rates are often available for **single** guests, and/or **children**. Prices are subject to change, so enquire with your hosts for confirmation of tariff and any reduced rates.

Children, smoking, pets, and suitable arrival and departure times, should be discussed with your host where relevant. Many B&Bs are smoke-free inside, and sometimes are not suitable for children. If you arrive late afternoon and leave around 10am you should be safe, but do check - some are more flexible than others. Some B&Bs offer an evening meal - again enquire with your hosts. **All evening meals are by arrangement** except where the property has its own restaurant. Please request meals well in advance - do not expect meals on demand.

Russell

Houhora
The Ranch House

Ruve and Stephen Nattrass
Tel: 09 4098824
Far North Road
Houhora
Fax: 09 4098824

Single: $30
Double/twin: $50-70
Breakfast: Continental
Beds: 2Q 2S
Evening meal: Not available
Bathrooms: 1EN 1GS

Stephen and Ruve extend an invitation to experience the enjoyment of harbourside accommodation in the beautiful Far North. Fishing, water sports, golf, Wagener museum, beachcombing are a few of many attractions. We are only meters from local wharf and restaurant, 15 minutes from popular Henderson Bay and Ravawa beach.

Kaitaia
Siesta Guest Lodge

Alan and Carole Harding
Tel: 09 4092011
Tasman Heights Road, Ahipara
Fax: 09 4092011
Mob: 025 965085
Email: Ninetymile@xtra.co.nz

Single: $100
Double/twin: $125
Breakfast: Cooked
Beds: 2Q
Evening meal: $35pp
Bathrooms: 2EN

The 'Siesta Guest Lodge' overlooks the sheltered Ahipara Bay and magnificent Ninety Mile Beach. Our Mediterranean style house is set in 3/4 acres of private grounds. The luxury guests wing is quiet, each unit has panoramic views, private balcony, TV, ensuite bathroom and tea & coffee making facility. Come and stay and we would love to direct you to all the wonderful places in the Far North!

Coopers Beach/Mangonui
Breaker House

Laurie Hilsgen   Chris Mathews
Tel: 09 4060412
319 SH 10, Cable Bay
Doubtless Bay
Fax: 09 4061036
Mob: 021 2776677
Email: 100245.3520@compuserve.com

Single: $225-250
Double/twin: $225-250
Breakfast: Special
Beds: 2Q
Evening meal: Not available
Bathrooms: 2EN

Built as holiday accommodation 30 years ago, Breaker House offers every luxury in a romantic, secluded, beachfront setting. There are two self-contained studios with private bathrooms and kitchen facilities, balconies overlooking Doubtless Bay and Cable Bay beach, timber floors, Tvs, stereos, videos, and laundry facilities. Tiered decks fringed by native pohutukawa trees ensure plenty of space to relax in a hammock, watch the dolphins, or bake a pizza in the wood-fired pizza oven (hosts provide the dough - just add your own toppings). Studios are decorated with antiques and contemporary New Zealand art and equipped with beach towels, fishing rods, boogie boards, books, videos, Cds, telephones and faxes. Bed linen featuring sea themes is by Mangonui artist Annie Tothill. Visit local attractions - kiwi and glow worm park, Maori pa sites, Butler House, kauri forest, Cape Reinga, historic Mangonui village with its world famous fish and chip shop - or hide away at Breaker House, swimming and snorkelling from private bays below the property. Breakfast (on the deck or in your unit) consists of homemade muesli with Northland macadamia nuts, seasonal fruits, bagels, plunger coffee/tea, and freshly squeezed juice.
Breaker House accepts all major credit and eftpos cards.

Doubtless Bay Lodge
Harry and Berwyn Porten **Double/twin:** $90
Tel: 09 4061661
33 Cable Bay Block Road, Coopers Beach
Fax: 09 4061662
Mob: 025 2752144

All new. Enjoy the seaside and the countryside.

Kaeo
June Sale Self-contained Accommodation
June Sale **Double/twin:** $60
Tel: 09 4050523
Te Ngaere Bay, Kaeo
Fax: 09 4050604
Mob: 025 903861

Self contained flat, 1m walk to lovely beach.

Broadwood
The Old Parish House
Mary Ridge **Double/twin:** $70
Awaroa Road, Broadwood
Hokianga
Tel: 09 4095500

Homely, comfortable, into crafts - patchwork, spinning, weaving etc.

Kerikeri
A Place to Be

Catherine Leonard   Bob Cooper **Single:** $45
Tel: 09 4075474 **Double/twin:** $80
Te Ra Road, Kerikeri **Breakfast:** Cooked
Fax: 09 4075474 **Beds:** 3D
Email: 100405.3626@Compuserve.com **Evening meal:** $25pp
 Bathrooms: 2EN 1PR

If you are coming to Northland we INSIST you visit with us. We are Takou Bay 5mins from the beach, high up overlooking the Cavalli Islands. The whole area is steeped in NZ history. Explore if you will or stay home with us and we'll spoil you a bit.

Graleen

Graeme and Colleen Wattam
Tel: 09 4079047
Kerikeri Road, Kerikeri
Fax: 09 4079047
Mob: 025 940845

Single: $40
Double/twin: $70
Breakfast: Cooked
Beds: 1Q 1D 2S
Evening meal: Not available
Bathrooms: 3EN

We invite you to join us, next to Rocket Café, 200 mtrs from SH 10 on Kerikeri Road. 2 mins airport, 3 mins Kerikeri town, 20 mins Paihia/Waitangi.

Jacaranda Lodge

Les Brocas   Ruth Anderson
Tel: 09 4076053
60 Cobham Road
Kerikeri

Double/twin: $75

Coopers Beach

Paihia
The Cedar Suite

Jo and Peter Nisbet
Tel: 09 4028516
5 Sullivan's Road, Central Paihia,
Bay of Islands
Fax: 09 4028555
Mob: 025 969281

Single: $81-110
Double/twin: $88-135
Breakfast: Continental
Beds: 5Q 3S
Evening meal: $25pp
Bathrooms: 5EN

For a homestay with a difference, The Cedar Suite offers friendliness and fun while you relax in our modern cedar home amid fairytale bush. Suites are separate with their own superior en suites. Peter has a career background with the New Zealand Symphony Orchestra and also enjoys cooking. Jo's interests range from photography to interior design. Our use of fresh produce from the Bay make breakfasts an enticing delight of many homemade creations. Guests have off-street parking, quality appointments and particularly comfortable beds, all within easy walking distance of Paihia's shops, tours and beaches. Also available is our charming, self-catering, character cottage, complete with period fittings, modern plumbing and kitchen. A track to the beach and a lovely view of the Bay make seaview cottage a place not to be missed at any time of the year. In all cases we suggest you book in advance.

Fairlight River Lodge

Anna and Michael Innes-Jones
Tel 09 4028004
107B Yorke Road
Haruru Falls
Paihia, Bay of Islands
Fax 09 4028048

Single: Enquire
Double/twin: $80-120
Breakfast: Continental
Beds: 2K 4S
Evening meal: Enquire
Bathrooms: 2EN 1GS

Fairlight is set on 2 acres of lawn on the banks of the Waitangi River and overlooking a native tree reserve. A bird watchers paradise. Perfect base for tours to Cape Reinga. Hole in the caves walk. Sailing. Wine tasting. Hot pools. River boat cruises. Fourth generation New Zealanders.

Paradise View
Iris Bartlett
Tel: 09 4028458
34 Selwyn Road, Paihia, Bay of Islands
Fax: 09 4028457

Double/twin: $95

Separate self-contained accommodation. Million dollar views, affordable rates.

Puketona Lodge
Heather and Maurice Pickup
Tel: 09 4028152
Puketona Road, Paihia, Bay of Islands
Fax: 09 4028152
Mob: 025 770833
Email: puketona@igrin.co.nz

Single: $80
Double/twin: $95-100
Breakfast: Cooked
Beds: 1K 1D
Evening meal: $30pp
Bathrooms: 1EN 1PR

Our modern home is close to historic Waitangi, Kerikeri and Waimate North. Tour buses can collect guests at our gate. Guest rooms are private and quiet. Note: King bed can be made up as two singles.

The Bush Hut
Tony and Averill Morris
Tel: 09 4027310
51 Seaview Road
Paihia
Bay of Islands
Fax: 09 4027310

Single: $50
Double/twin: $80
Breakfast: Continental
Beds: 1Q 1S
Evening meal: Not available
Bathrooms: 1PR

A warm welcome awaits you in your quiet studio unit, which is close to beach, village and departure points for tourist trips.
Will meet coaches.

Russell
Ounuwhao

Allan and Marilyn Nicklin
Tel: 09 4037310
Matauwhi Bay, Russell
Bay of Islands
Fax: 09 4037310

Single: $60
Double/twin: $95-120
Breakfast: Special
Beds: 4Q 4S
Evening meal: Not available
Bathrooms: 2EN 1GS

Our century-old, fully restored kauri homestead has been decorated in old-fashioned, victorian-style, with brass beds, patchwork quilts and garden fresh flowers to greet you on arrival. Afternoon tea is complementary. We have four beautiful double guest-rooms, with quality linens and towels, and each with its own special character to make your stay with us unique and memorable. We are located opposite the sea, where many yachts are moored, alongside a reserve, and only a 10 min flat walk to the historic Russell village. Our cottage garden is a special delight in spring and summer - you are welcome to sit and share it with us. Home-baked goodies will tantalise your tastebuds for breakfast. Wake to the smell of fresh bread or muffins. We pride ourselves on our special, all home-made preserves and muesli, freshly brewed coffee or tea. A nostalgic, peaceful holiday is guaranteed. Our home is smoke-free. We are closed June/July. We also have a delightful 1930's self-contained cottage for guests to stay. Please enquire - sleeps 4 persons maximum.

Brown Lodge
Roly and Joan Brown   **Double/twin:** $160
Tel: 09 4037693
6 Ashby Street, Russell, Bay of Islands
Fax: 09 4037683
Unique, central, seaviews, quality ensuites, ambience, antiques, airconditioning.

Lesley's B&B
Lesley Coleman   **Double/twin:** $85
Tel: 09 4037099
Pomare Road, Russell, Bay of Islands
Email: mend@voyager.co.nz

Full English breakfast. Ten minutes walk to town.

Mako Lodge and Fishing Charters

Graeme and Jean McIntosh **Double/twin:** $95-150
Tel: 09 4037770
Te Wahapu Road, Russell, Bay of Islands
Fax: 09 4037770
Mob: 025 739787
Free: 0800 625669
Email: mako.lodge-charters@clear.net.nz

Private waterfront location. Optional charter fishing/sightseeing package.

Te Wahapu Homestead

Robin and Jill Colquhoun **Single:** $80-120
Tel: 09 4037464 **Double/twin:** $80-120
Te Wahapu Beach, Russell **Breakfast:** Cooked
Bay of Islands **Beds:** 1K 1Q 2S
Fax: 09 4037464 **Evening meal:** Not available
Mob: 025 733549 **Bathrooms:** 1GS

Historic homestead (c1843). Absolute waterfront. Peace and tranquility assured. Self contained cottage sleeps four. Boat and fishing gear available (no extra charge). Bookings essential.

Tokouru

Michael and Robin Watson **Double/twin:** $100
Tel: 09 4037458
21 Titore Way, Russell, Bay of Islands
Mob: 025 765459
Email: mikerobe@igrin.co.nz
Sea, views, bush, walks, town and restaurants close.

Kaikohe
Taraire Grove

Lewis and Joy Sandford **Single:** $50
Tel: 09 4010623 **Double/twin:** $75
SH 12, Kaikohe **Breakfast:** Cooked
 Beds: 2S
 Evening meal: $28pp
 Bathrooms: 1PR

Located 25 minutes from the beautiful Bay of Islands, 30 minutes from west coast beaches. Situated centrally to the great attractions of the far north of New Zealand.

Omapere
Dawn Bed & Breakfast

Alan and Gaye Dawn **Single:** $50
Tel: 09 4058773 **Double/twin:** $80-90
Signal Station Road, Omapere **Breakfast:** Continental
Fax: 09 4058773 **Beds:** 1D 2S
 Evening meal: $35pp
 Bathrooms: 1EN 1GS

Explore the Kauri forests and coastal walks; come sailing; recharge. Share our home with fantastic views and peaceful, bird-filled gardens. Fully self-contained apartment also available.

Whaley B&B

Alexa and Owen Whaley **Double/twin:** $70
Tel: 09 4058641
Signal Station Road, Omapere
Fax: 09 4058643
Friendly hosts; a view in a million.

Dargaville
Kauri Ridge Homestay

Agnes and Wallace Bennett
Tel: 09 4395163
RD 2, Dargaville

Double/twin: $60

Whangarei
Karamea House

Tony and Cherry Hopkins
Tel: 09 4353401
Apotu Road, Kamo, Whangarei
Fax: 09 4353495
Mob: 025 2764096
Email: tonyhopkins@clear.net.nz

Single: $90
Double/twin: $125
Breakfast: Cooked
Beds: 2Q 1D 1S
Evening meal: $30pp
Bathrooms: 1FS

Welcome to Karamea House. This magnificient colonial homestead is set in total privacy but is only 12 minutes north of Whangarei and just 2 kms off State Highway 1. It is ideally positioned to visit the beautiful east coast bays and less than an hour from the Bay of Islands. Although conveniently located, we offer peace and quiet in a rural setting surrounded by beautiful grounds and paddocks with pet lambs and horses. Excellent amenities include an all weather astroturf tennis court, swimming pool and outdoor spa pool. The two storey house features open fireplaces as well as central heating, a formal dining room, two lounges, a study and a huge country style kitchen. Guests enjoy exclusive use of the first floor. A separate barn is available for sleeping accommodation on request. Dinner is available and, of course, a generous breakfast is provided. We have both travelled extensively and enjoy welcoming guests from home and abroad.

Ballater Lodge

Bill and Rosie Sanderson
Tel: 09 4346514
Maungatapere
Fax: 09 4300278
Mob: 025 959165
Email: ballater@clear.net.nz

Single: $50
Double/twin: $80-100
Breakfast: Continental
Beds: 1K 1D
Evening meal: $25pp
Bathrooms: 1EN 1PR

Ballater lodge, luxury self contained accomodation, 10 minutes from Whangarei set in an 18 acre Avocado orchard in the heart of the stone wall country.

Brigadoon

Shane and Sheila Holland
Tel: 09 4365772
Ritchie Road, Parua Bay, Whangarei

Double/twin: $55

Cottage gardens, close to beach and golf course.

City Lights Whangarei

Kevin McMahon   Doug Simpson
Tel: 09 4382390
40A Vale Road, Riverside
Whangarei
Fax: 09 4382390
Mob: 025 958243

Single: $40
Double/twin: $70
Breakfast: Cooked
Beds: 1K 1Q 2S
Evening meal: Not available
Bathrooms: 1EN 1GS

Views over city & river. Walk to town basin. Meet boxers Cass & Cara and P4 the cat. No smoking inside. Not suitable for children. Phone booking essential.

Koinonia Manor

Allan and Adele Kimber
Tel: 09 4375961
260 Ngunguru Road
Whangarei

Single: $40
Double/twin: $70
Breakfast: Special
Beds: 2D 3S
Evening meal: $25pp
Bathrooms: 1GS 1FS

Three kilometres beyond Whangarei Falls, we are situated enroute to the wonderful Tutukaka coast. Come, enjoy the charm of yesteryear. Dining alfresco, barbecuing or intimate candlelight are specialties.

McLeod Bay Self-contained Unit

Margaret Wilson
Tel: 09 4340577
1903 Whangarei Heads Road,
McLeod Bay
Whangarei

Single: $45
Double/twin: $60
Breakfast: Special
Beds: 1D
Evening meal: Not available
Bathrooms: 1EN

Magnificent sea and rural views. Beach frontage.
Garden setting. Double sofa bed also available.

Oakura Bay Bed & Breakfast

Neil and Diane McKay
Tel: 09 4336066
24 Rapata Road
Oakura
Fax: 09 4336066

Single: $20-30
Double/twin: $40-60
Breakfast: Continental
Beds: 1D 2S
Evening meal: $20pp
Bathrooms: 1FS

Visit our beautiful safe beach and harbour 50 kms north east of Whangarei on the coastal route to Russell. Kayaks for hire. Backpackers welcome.

Pukepoto Orchards

Janet and Dave McNaughton
Tel: 09 4375433
521 Ngunguru Road
Glenbervie,
Whangarei
Fax: 09 4373533

Single: $30-40
Double/twin: $60-65
Breakfast: Special
Beds: 2S
Evening meal: Not available
Bathrooms: 1EN

Enjoy a stay in our spacious self-contained unit, surrounded by garden, swimming pool, kiwifruit orchard. 15 minutes from beautiful Tutukaka coast beaches and 10 minutes to Whangarei.

Vealbrook Cottage

Pretoria and Bob Sturge
Tel: 09 4340098
McLeods Bay, Whangarei Heads
Fax: 09 4340098

Double/twin: $70

Outstanding harbour view. Accommodation for 8 including self contained flat.

Tutukaka
Brimar Lodge

Brian and Marion Slater
Tel: 09 4343951
1890 Ngunguru Road
Tutukaka Coast
Fax: 09 4344951
Email: nz.desdive@xtra.co.nz

Single: $40-60
Double/twin: $75-130
Breakfast: Cooked
Beds: 2K 1D 2S
Evening meal: $20pp
Bathrooms: 2EN 1GS

Brimar Lodge is a large sunny house sitting on the beach estuary at Ngunguru which is situated 5 minutes away from Tutukaka - the gateway to the Poor Knight Islands - a scuba divers paradise.
All visitors and tourists welcome - tariff reduction for groups and backpackers. NZ wide diving holidays and accommodation arranged.

Glengarry

Bet and Noel Glengarry
Tel: 09 4343646
Ngunguru, RD 3
Whangarei

Double/twin: $65

Comfortable homestay at beach. 25kms from Whangarei.

Ruakaka
Camellia House

Eunice and Jim Bratty
Tel: 09 4328138
1 Camellia Avenue,
Ruakaka

Single: $40
Double/twin: $60
Breakfast: Cooked
Beds: 1D 2S
Evening meal: Enquire
Bathrooms: 1GS

Private back yard for relaxing. Sea views and beach walks.
Five minutes from golf course and race course.

Langs Beach
Lochalsh

Graham and Billie Long
Tel: 09 4320053
Langs Beach, Waipu
Fax: 09 4320053

Double/twin: $80-90

You don't get closer to the beach than this.

Mangawhai
Lake View Chalets

Arnim Pierau   Gabi Manschewski
Tel: 09 4314086
662 Ocean View Road, Te Arai Point,
Wellsford
Fax: 09 4314326
Free: 0800 525384
Email: gabi.m@xtra.co.nz

Single: $100
Double/twin: $120
Breakfast: Extra charge $8pp
Beds: 6K 12S
Evening meal: Not available
Bathrooms: 6PR

We are situated on 80 ha of farmland surrounding beautiful Spectacle and Slipper Lake. Each Chalet is individually positioned for maximum privacy, with superb views over either Spectacle or Slipper Lake. Designed for maximum comfort and relaxation, your chalets will make you feel at home. The Chalets are tastefully furnished and decorated, featuring a timber ceiling and tiled floors.

Fallowfield
Jean and Don Goldschmidt **Double/twin:** $85
Tel: 09 4315096
Stainforth Road, Mangawhai
Fax: 09 4315063
Mob: 025 829736

Private, coastal views, country retreat, warm hospitality, dinner.

Mangawhai Lodge
Jeannette Forde
Tel: 09 4315311
4 Heather Street, Mangawhai Heads
Fax: 09 4315312
Mob: 025 2712790
Email: the.lodge@xtra.co.nz

Single: $60-85
Double/twin: $85-130
Breakfast: Cooked
Beds: 2K 2Q 6S
Evening meal: Not available
Bathrooms: 2EN 1PR 1FS

A colonial lodge, opposite a championship golf course and café, offering spectacular sea views off wide verandahs surrounding this elegant spacious house. Business representatives welcome

Warkworth
Belvedere Homestay
Margaret and Ron Everett
Tel: 09 4257201
38 Kanuka Road, Sandspit
Fax: 09 4257201
Mob: 025 2844771

Single: $45
Double/twin: $80-90
Breakfast: Continental
Beds: 1Q 1D
Evening meal: $30pp
Bathrooms: 1EN 1GS

Located 7 ks from Warkworth on the coast where the ferries leave for Kawau. 360 degree view, air conditioned, games room, spa pool. 11 acres of peace and quiet.

Mahurangi Lodge
Alison and Rodney Woodcock **Double/twin:** $50-70
Tel: 09 4255465
416 Mahurangi East Road,
Snells Beach
Fax: 09 4255465

Superb views, marine reserve nearby, Kawau cruise discount available, 1 1/2hrs Airport.

'Rather see the wonders of the world abroad than, living dully sluggardized at home, wear out thy youth with shapeless idleness.' - **Shakespeare**

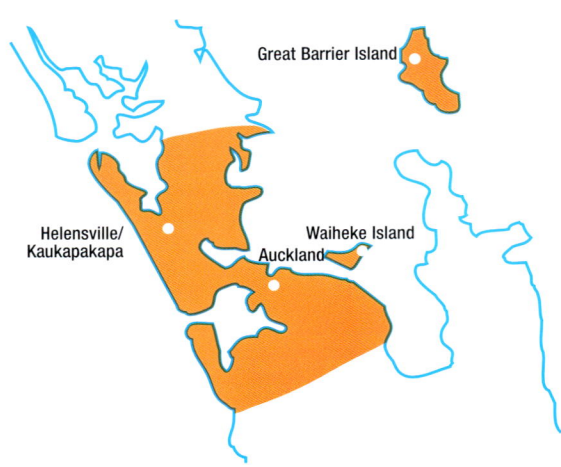

Note: Auckland listings are in 2 sections
Auckland City = within 5km of CPO page 19-26
Auckland = outside 5km radius page 26-30

Helensville/Kaukapakapa
Kaipara House
John and Diane Barrett
Tel: 09 4207462
Cnr Hwy 16 & Parkhurst Rd, Parakai
Fax: 09 4207458
Mob: 025 814617

Single: $45
Double/twin: $80
Breakfast: Continental
Beds: 1D 2S
Evening meal: $20pp
Bathrooms: 1FS

Today we greet you with yesterdays fully restored 1890's villa with todays colours in your Victorian or Edwardian rooms and of course our young personalities!

Kereru Lodge
Betty Headford
Tel: 09 4205223
Arone Farm, Makarau Road, Kaukapakapa
Fax: 09 4205223

Double/twin: $65

Malolo House
Andrea Mullin
Tel: 09 4207262
110 Commercial Road,
Helensville
Fax: 09 4207262
Mob: 025 2803008
Email: malolo@xtra.co.nz

Double/twin: $85

Lovingly restored villa in heart of historic Helensville.

Auckland City
Amberley Bed & Breakfast

Mary and Michael Burnett
Tel: 09 4460506
3 Ewen Alison Avenue, Devonport
Auckland
Fax: 09 4460506
Email: amberley@xtra.co.nz

Single: $70-90
Double/twin: $90-120
Breakfast: Special
Beds: 3Q 2S
Evening meal: Not available
Bathrooms: 2GS

Our home, an elegant colonial villa, nestled at the base of Mt Victoria is within easy walking distance of Devonport's numerous cafes, shops, safe beaches, golf course, and ferry terminal. (A 10min. Ride to downtown Auckland). Spectacular panoramic views from the summit of Mt Victoria. Bedrooms are spacious and charmingly furnished. Two guest bathrooms (one with double Spabath). Bathrobes are provided. If arriving on an early flight, please feel free to relax in our large guest lounge with complimentary tea/coffee making facilities, guest frig and homebaking. (A shuttle service is available from airport approx NZ$17 ea) Laundry facilities available. A delicious breakfast is served in our spacious diningroom with city views. We have travelled extensively both here and overseas and we look forward to meeting you and making your stay in our beautiful country an enjoyable and unforgettable experience. Bankcards: Visa, Bankcard, Amex.
Location: Turn right at Mt Victoria roundabout, go 200 mtrs, then first right at Victoria Superette corner.

Jeong-K Place by the Sea

Jeong Sook Kim and Kazuko Inaba
Tel: 09 4451358
4 King Edward Parade, Devonport
Auckland
Fax: 09 4461358
Mob: 025 889276
Email: jeong-k@ihug.co.nz

Single: $170-190
Double/twin: $190-210
Breakfast: Special
Beds: 3Q 2S
Evening meal: $60-70pp
Bathrooms: 4EN

The Edwardian villa, located on the Devonport promenade, features kauri flooring and an extensive balcony and verandah facing the harbour where world-class yachts sail by. This beachfront home, originally built circa 1900, has been refurbished and upgraded with a central heating system and fire sprinklers to provide a safe, warm, cosy and high quality serviced guest house to today's discerning travlellers. Four ensuite guest rooms open individually into the shady garden with its mature trees. Complimentary fresh coffee and tea, port and NZ wines are served in the timber floored sea view lounge with pleasant sea breeze. Our gourmet breakfast is freshly prepared with good quality produce and is served in the elegant dining room that overlooks a tranquil garden and Waitemata Harbour. Jeong Sook and Kazuo are trained chefs, serving different breakfasts each day from a varied cooked menu which includes crab-meat puff, hot spring eggs, okonomiyaki, eggs benedict, waffles and pancakes of course with fresh fruits. Dinner is only served by prior arrangement.
The ferry terminal (8 minutes ride to central Auckland) is within a minutes walk. Plenty of car parks.

The Peace & Plenty Inn

Carol and Graham Ward
Tel: 09 4452925
6 Flagstaff Terrace,
Devonport, Auckland
Fax: 09 4452901

Single: $180
Double/twin: $210
Breakfast: Special
Beds: 5Q 1S
Evening meal: Not available
Bathrooms: 5EN

Peace and Plenty Inn extends a world or romance, graciousness, fine food and hospitality. Situated in an unbeatable location, the property is on the waterfront in the historic village of Devonport, only minutes by ferry from the city. Stroll to the beaches, cafes, fascinating shops, museums and art galleries. A magnificently restored 1880's Victorian residence, Peace and Plenty offers five luxurious queen size rooms, decorated in French provincial style, all with ensuites. Breakfast is a gourmet affair, with free range eggs, double smoked bacon and freshly squeezed orange juice. Start your day with homemade yoghurt and muesli, fresh muffins, eggs Benedict, French baked eggs, waffles, smoked salmon, scrambled eggs etc. with a selection of teas and coffee. A delightful seaside village whose colonial history is unspoilt by the passage of time. One of Auckland's earliest settlements. Devonport exudes charm and civility with beautifully restored old homes, over 30 restaurants and cafes, and excellent shopping, all only 10 minutes by frequent ferry service or 20 minutes by car from central Auckland. Discover our small town in the heart of the city with broad beaches, historic walks, extinct volcanoes, exciting harbour and city vistas, boats, museums, art galleries, theatre and an 18 hole golf course.

Carol and Graham Ward have more than 30 year's experience in service industries - Carol in retail and café ownership, Graham with an international airline and a multi-national logistics company. Devonport residents for 32 years, they have also travelled extensively and lived for brief periods in the Pacific Islands and Asia. Peace and Plenty Inn offers tranquillity and fine food in luxurious surroundings, a perfect setting for newlyweds, business executives and travellers.

From Auckland Airport take the airport shuttle bus direct to our door, or if driving, follow directions to Devonport via highway one across the harbour bridge.
Enter Flagstaff Terrace, off the main street (Victoria Road in the centre of the village.
We are the first house and we welcome you.

Amersham House

Jill and Robin Stirling
Tel: 09 3030321
1 Canterbury Place, Parnell
Auckland
Fax: 09 3030621
Email: stirling@xtra.co.nz

Single: $160
Double/twin: $160-280
Breakfast: Cooked
Beds: 1K 1Q 2D 1S
Evening meal: $45-55pp
Bathrooms: 4EN

"Romantic and private". Luxurious bedrooms have Sky TV, phones, spa or sauna and with the library/dayroom they enjoy sun and stunning harbour views. Walk to the city or relax around our heated pool & spa complex and finish the day with a glass of wine with your NZ hosts.

Bakers' Place B&B Garden Cottage

Mike and Pauline Baker
Tel: 09 4454035
30 Hastings Parade, Devonport
Auckland
Fax: 09 4454035
Mob: 021 2166450
Email: baker@ihug.co.nz

Single: $85
Double/twin: $120
Breakfast: Cooked
Beds: 1K
Evening meal: Not available
Bathrooms: 1EN

A "Magical", hideaway nestled amidst native trees in a private secluded garden. The cottage has its own kitchen and laundry facilities. TV and ozone sterilized spa. A 5 minutes stroll to Devonport Village, restaurants, cafes and museums, beaches and golf course. Downtown Auckland City is just 12 minutes by ferry.
Note: King bed can be made up as two singles.

Bavaria B&B Hotel

Rudi Schmidt and Ulrike Stephan
Tel: 09 6389641
83 Valley Road, Mt Eden
Aucklland
Fax: 09 6389665

Single: $78
Double/twin: $110
Breakfast: Special
Beds: 7Q 4S
Evening meal: Not available
Bathrooms: 11EN

We offer quality B&B accommodation in quiet residential surroundings yet, are located only 2 km from the city centre which can be easily reached by bus or car. All our friendly 11 non-smoker rooms have ensuites and telephones. Relax on our sunny deck and enjoy our extensive breakfast buffet. Off-street parking available.

Birkenhead Bay Lodge

Claire and Kris Metcalf
Tel: 09 4802891
43 Rawene Road,
Birkenhead Point

Single: Enquire
Double/twin: $150
Breakfast: Special
Beds: 2Q
Evening meal: Not available
Bathrooms: 1GS

Birkenhead Bay Lodge is located within close walking distance to Birkenheads trendy cafes, boutique shops and restaurants. Catering mainly to couples who want a special night away we offer luxury accommodation, scrumptious breakfasts and guests will have breathtaking views of Auckland City from their balcony. Reservations essential. Non-smoking household.

Colonial Cottage

Grae Glieu
Tel: 09 3602820
35 Clarence Street,
Ponsonby, Auckland
Fax: 09 3603436

Single: $100 +
Double/twin: $100 +
Breakfast: Special
Beds: 2D 1S
Evening meal: $25pp
Bathrooms: 1GS

Turn-of-the-century Kauri villa offers olde-worlde charm, warmth, comfort, quiet, and modern amenities in the heartbeat of the city. Adjacent to Herne Bay, Ponsonby Café mile and quality restaurants. Airport Shuttle service door-to-door. Handy to public transport, city attractions and motorways. Alternative health therapies and massage available. Special dietary requirements catered for.
Note: Exclusive occupancy $250 +.

Aniwaniwa Cottage Homestay / Motel

Peter Goldsbury and family
Tel: 09 4454454
20 Hastings Parade,
Devonport
Fax: 09 4454454
Email: pgoldsbury@stratex.co.nz

Single: $70
Double/twin: $100
Breakfast: Continental
Beds: 1Q 4S
Evening meal: Not available
Bathrooms: 1GS

Families or groups. Make our colonial home, garden, pool in picturesque Devonport yours. Everything supplied. Full kitchen. Safe, short stroll to restaurants, downtown ferry, beaches. Extra guests $30pp. Note: Additional single beds available on request.

Badger's of Devonport

Heather and Badger Miller
Tel: 09 4452099
30 Summer Street, Devonport
Fax: 09 4450231
Email: badgers@clear.net.nz

Double/twin: $119-135

Victorian villa, en-suites, teddy bears, chocolates, sumptuous breakfasts.

Greenlane Homestay

Clare Ross   Win Dickey
Tel: 09 5233419
21 Atarangi Road, Greenlane
Auckland
Fax: 09 5248506
Free: 0800 254419

Single: $40
Double/twin: $65
Breakfast: Cooked
Beds: 2Q 2S
Evening meal: $12.50pp
Bathrooms: 1GS 1FS

Comfortable non smoking home with modern facilities close to Cornwall Park and One Tree Hill. Downtown 10 minutes, airport 20. Tea, coffee and TV - all times.

Parituhu

Helen Mackenzie   Lyndsay Rendall
Tel: 09 4456559
3 King Edward Parade, Devonport
Auckland
Fax: 09 4456559
Email: parituhu@iprolink.co.nz

Single: $60
Double/twin: $80
Breakfast: Continental
Beds: 1Q
Evening meal: Not available
Bathrooms: 1PR

Our comfortable 75 year old bungalow is 50 metres from a swimming beach and 5 minutes easy walk to restaurants, shops and ferry to downtown Auckland.

Rawene Homestay

Dorothy and Ron Bebarfald
Tel: 09 4800206
10 Rawene Road, Birkenhead
Auckland
Fax: 09 4800306

Single: $60
Double/twin: $70-80
Breakfast: Continental
Beds: 1K 2S
Evening meal: Not available
Bathrooms: 1PR

Ron and Dorothy offer comfortable, self-contained flat, separate entrance and parking, 5 minutes walk to Highbury restaurants, shopping mall and buses to Takapuna and Auckland city.

Sedgwick Kent Lodge

Wout and Helma van der Lans
Tel: 09 5245219
65 Lucerne Road, Remuera
Auckland
Fax: 09 5204825
Email: accommodation@sedgwick.co.nz

Single: $145-160
Double/twin: $160-175
Breakfast: Special
Beds: 4Q 1D 3S
Evening meal: $65pp
Bathrooms: 5EN

Restored 1910 homestead with stained glass windows and native timbers. Elegance and warm hospitality complimented by antique furniture, oriental rugs and original paintings.

The Garden Room

Perrine and Bryan Hall
Tel: 09 4452472
23 Cheltenham Road, Devonport
Auckland
Fax: 09 4452472
Mob: 025 989643
Email: b.hall@clear.net.nz

Double/twin: $135

Private sunny self-contained cottage in lovely garden by beach.

Wharemoana B&B

Red and Jan Potts
Tel: 09 4457549
4A North Avenue, Devonport
Auckland

Double/twin: $75

Close to beaches, bus, Devonport restaurants, cafes, ferry.

Wheturangi House

Ruth and Roger Genet
Tel: 09 5294447
94 Wheturangi Road, Greenlane
Auckland
Fax: 09 5295044
Email: genet@xtra.co.nz

Single: $100-130
Double/twin: Enquire
Breakfast: Cooked
Beds: 1K 1D 1S
Evening meal: $30pp
Bathrooms: 2EN

Separate guest accommodation. Cottage garden. 15 mins - airport, beaches, city. 5 mins - restaurants, theatres, racetracks, hospitals, one tree hill. Delicious breakfast. Fresh coffee, baking, flowers.

The Lookouts

Paul and Jenny Steele
Tel 09 4281400
Waterside Crescent,
Gulf Harbour, Auckland
Fax 09 4281400

Single: $120-250
Double/twin: $120-250
Breakfast: Enquire
Beds: 1K 1Q 1D 2S
Evening meal: $30pp
Bathrooms: 3EN

A stunning Mediterranean retreat situated above the boat laden canal of Gulf Harbour is truly a GOLFING and AQUATIC paradise. From our comfortably appointed and spacious highrise apartment there are panoramic views of Sky Tower, the north shore, Kawau Island and the Gulf Harbour Country Club (venue of the 1998 World Cup of Golf). Play can be arranged mostly at discounted rates. Restaurants within strolling distance or easy driving. N.Z. style dinners cooked by arrangement after the first night. We offer a complimentary tour of the local highlights. Safe swimming beaches nearby. Three double ensuite bedrooms, one with a balcony overlooking the canal ensure privacy. Sauna available. Ferry trips to Auckland and the award winning Tiri Tiri Matangi Island bird sanctuary start at our door. We can do Airport pickups. We have a maximum of four guests at any one time. Please phone for further information and tariff.

Birchwood

Ann and Mike Davies
Tel: 09 2928729
Clevedon,
Auckland South
Fax: 09 2928555

Single: $165
Double/twin: $165-195
Breakfast: Special
Beds: 1K 2Q
Evening meal: Not available
Bathrooms: 1EN 1PR 1GS

Ann and Mike invite you to go back in time to a leisurely and gracious way of life. Enjoy the romance and intimacy of this restored country B & B surrounded by lush green pastures and a large rambling garden. Constructed using NZ native timbers, this two-storeyed villa is furnished with a delicate mingling of old and new. The King bed and two Queen beds in the private guest wing offers the ultimate in away from home comfort - fresh flowers, quality bedding, robes and special touches. Tantalize your taste buds with freshly squeezed orange juice, fruits in season, homemade yoghurt and muesli, and of course something from the oven; all served with coffee and a selection of teas. Stroll through the garden, laze by the pool or just relax and reminisce - savour the pastoral setting. Complimentary sherry and port. Birchwood is located on the outskirts of the Clevedon Village near restaurants, craftshops, golf-courses, polo grounds, tourist trails and beaches. Farm activities such as horse riding and sheep-shearing can be arranged. Treat yourself - enjoy country charm centrally located.

811 Bed & Breakfast

David Fitchew   Bryan Condon
Tel: 09 6204284
811 Dominion Road, Mt Eden
Auckland
Fax: 09 6204286
Mob: 025 2898863

Single: $45
Double/twin: $65
Breakfast: Special
Beds: 2D 2S
Evening meal: Not available
Bathrooms: 2GS

Guests say: A lovely laid back atmosphere and I was made to feel at home. Excellent restaurants close by. Bus to Auckland centre at gate.

Aspen House

Margaret Cooper
Tel: 09 5799391
1/94 Celtic Cres, Ellerslie, Auckland
Fax: 09 5210708

Double/twin: $50

Close to motorway and Ellerslie convention centre.

Beachfront Bed & Breakfast

Doreen Patten
Tel: 09 4784358
484A Beach Road, Murrays Bay, Auckland
Fax: 09 4787514

Double/twin: $70-100

Sea/Beach views.   15 mins from the city.

Camperdown Farmstay
Chris and David Hempleman
Tel: 09 4159009
455 Coatesville/Riverhead Hwy, Albany, Auckland
Fax: 09 4159023
Mob: 025 727108

Double/twin: $95

Tranquil tudor home and gardens. Tennis court. Pet lambs.

Cherrywood Homestay
Celeste Robison
Tel: 09 4442866
9 Gladys Avenue,
Glenfield
Auckland

Single: $35
Double/twin: $70
Breakfast: Cooked
Beds: 3S
Evening meal: $10pp
Bathrooms: 1PR

Attractive 'Swiss Chalet' home in a picturesque tree-fringed garden setting. Close to restaurants, beaches and theatre. 15 minutes to Takapuna - 20 minutes from Auckland.

Cockle Bay Homestays
Jill and Richard Paxman
Tel: 09 5350120
81 Pah Road, Cockle Bay, Howick, Auckland
Fax: 09 5350120
Mob: 021 685638
Email: PaxmanR@xtra.co.nz

Double/twin: $75-90

Amazing seaviews, quiet location, personal attention, warm welcome.

Curreen Homestay
Ron and Doreen Curreen
Tel: 09 5799531
39B Konini Road, One Tree Hill, Auckland
Fax: 09 5799531

Double/twin: $60-75

Large self-contained unit close to all amenities (quiet).

Glen Connor
Margaret Nikiel
Tel: 09 2360417
Paparata Road, Bombay, Auckland South

Double/twin: $60

Gulfview Self Contained Apartment
Peter Banks
Tel: 09 5365541
74 Craig Road, Maraetai Beach, Manukau
Fax: 09 5365580
Mob: 025 2852115
Email: pbanks@ihug.co.nz

Double/twin: $100

Views, beaches, golf, fishing, tramping, country living, restaurants.

Hawkless Bed & Breakfast
Jim and Andrea Hawkless
Tel: 09 4128862
45 Trigg Road, Huapai
Fax: 09 4128869

Double/twin: $70

Close, vineyards, beach, Auckland (30mins) rural, quiet

Kauri Valley Homestead B&B
Lynda Morrison Double/twin: $85
Tel: 09 4184634
39 Waipa Street, Birkenhead, Auckland
Email: lynda.m@xtra.co.nz

Spacious sunfilled home, farm-like surroundings, minutes north of city.

La Mer
Catherine and Mike Double/twin: $75-87
Tel: 09 5365447
6 Campbell Rd, Maraetai , Manukau
Fax: 09 5365638
Mob: 025 982419

Fully self contained, kayak rentals, sea views.

Mallee B&B Homestay
Malcolm McDonald Double/twin: $100-120
Tel: 09 8176252
36 Tinopai Road, Titirangi, Auckland
Mob: 021 687673

Spectacular views, beautiful setting, bush walks, beaches nearby.

Nor West Greenlands
Kay Hamilton Double/twin: $110
Tel: 09 4128167
303 Riverhead Road, Kumeu
Fax: 09 4128167
Mob: 025 2866064
Email: bed@farm-stay.co.nz

20kms Auckland. Sheep, bush stream, flowers, swimming pool.

Skovholm Country Lodge
Helge and Kathie Kristiansen
Tel: 09 4118326
78 Hinau Road
Waimauku
Fax: 09 4118326

Single: Enquire
Double/twin: $120-165
Breakfast: Special
Beds: 1K 1Q 1D 4S
Evening meal: Not available
Bathrooms: 2EN 1PR 1GS

Luxurious Bed & Breakfast -
1912 Homestead hidden away in 12 acres of native bush and country gardens - 1/2 hour NW Auckland City. A haven of peace & tranquility.

The Totara
Peter and Jeanne Maxwell Double/twin: $120
Tel: 09 5753514
1/17 Glover Road, St Heliers, Auckland
Fax: 09 5753582
Mob: 025 2840172

Warm friendly accommodation 15 minutes from Downtown.

Appletree Cottage
Marion Stokes Double/twin: $75-85
Tel: 09 3726647
33 Kiwi Street, Oneroa
Internet www.ki-wi.co.nz/appletre.htm

Top of the Hill Country Homestay

Trevor and Pat Simpson
Tel: 09 5308576
Fitzpatrick Road, Brookby, RD 1 Manurewa
Fax: 09 5308576
Email: topofthehill@nzhomestay.co.nz

Single: $65
Double/twin: $100
Breakfast: Cooked
Beds: 1Q 5S
Evening meal: $25pp
Bathrooms: 4EN

An expansive modern new country Homestay for the adventurous traveller who likes to get off the beaten track but still needs to be close to Auckland city.

Waiheke Island
Gulf Haven

Alan Ramsbottom   Lois Baucke
Tel: 09 3726629
49 Great Barrier Road,
Enclosure Bay
Fax: 09 3728558

Single: $65
Double/twin: $80-155
Breakfast: Continental
Beds: 1K 2Q 1D
Evening meal: Not available
Bathrooms: 2EN 1GS

Situated in a peaceful 2 acre garden with its own private seashore. We offer exclusive accommodation in either two self-contained Studio Apartments ($155) or Bed and Breakfast homestay($80-$95). Gulf Haven has dramatic unobstructed sea views from Waiheke beaches and headlands to Coromandel Peninsula and Great Barrier Island. Relax and enjoy friendly hospitality on our beautiful Island with its superb scenery and mild climate - just 20 kms from downtown Auckland where ferries leave every 2 hours. We meet you off the ferry. NB: Tariff for the studio apartments does not include breakfast

Cedar House

Anne Waymouth
Tel: 09 3725407
69 Queens Drive, Oneroa
Mob: 021 328817

Single: $30
Double/twin: $60

Totally S.C. Unit. Gulf views. Close to everything.

Herbs' Patch Homestay

Geoff and Val Herbert
Tel: 09 3729937
68 Hauraki Road
Palm Beach
Mob: 025 314462

Double/twin: $75-85

Spectacular views, full breakfast, petanque, free transfers.

Kowhai Close
Joyce and Guy Camilleri
Tel: 09 3726763
92 Nick Johnstone Drive,
Oneroa
Fax: 09 3726763
Email: kowhaicl@clear.net.nz

Single: $70
Double/twin: $90-150
Breakfast: Continental
Beds: 1Q 2D 2S
Evening meal: Not available
Bathrooms: 1EN 1GS

Enjoy rolling hills, seaview, coastal walks. We offer one self contained apartment or bed and breakfast homestay - close to the Mudbrick restaurant in tranquil and private surroundings.

Miro Vineyard
Catherine Vosper
Tel: 09 3727854
Browns Rd, Onetangi
Fax: 09 3727056
Email: miro@xtra.co.nz

Double/twin: $90

The villa on the vineyard by the sea.

Punga Lodge
Dyan Sharland   Rob Johnston
Tel: 09 3726675
223 Ocean View Road
Little Oneroa
Fax: 09 3726675

Double/twin: $90-115

Bush setting, 150m to beach, 1k to shops, also units.

Tiri Crest
Julie and Noel Thompson
Tel: 09 3725423
16 Tiri Road,
Oneroa
Mob: 025 2235805

Single: $50-85
Double/twin: $65-125
Breakfast: Continental
Beds: 1Q 1D 1S
Evening meal: Not available
Bathrooms: 1PR

Tiri Crest complex is self-contained, set in a pretty garden with lovely seaviews. Furnishings are modern and comfortable. Close to beach, village and transport. Note: Alternative phone number 09 5284794.

Twin Gables
Anne and Peter Thornbury
Tel: 09 3729877
17 Tiri Road,
Oneroa

Single: $40-45
Double/twin: $70-90
Breakfast: Continental
Beds: 1Q 1D 2S
Evening meal: Not available
Bathrooms: 1GS 1FS

Comfortable spacious rooms with sea views. Tea and coffee making facilities. Barbeque. Close to beach, shops, cafes. Pick up and return to the ferry.

Great Barrier Island
Tipi and Bob's Waterfront Lodge
Peter and Margery Harris
Tel: 09 4290550
Puriri Bay, Tryphena
Fax: 09 4290550

Double/twin: $114-144

COROMANDEL/BAY OF PLENTY/EAST COAST/HAWKES BAY/WAIRARAPA PAGES 32 - 51

Coromandel
Whitianga
Tairua
Whangamata
Thames
Waihi
Katikati
Mt Maunganui/Papamoa
Te Puke
Matamata Tauranga
Whakatane/Ohope
Opotiki
Tolaga Bay
Lake Waikaremoana
Gisborne
Wairoa Mahia
Napier
Hastings/Havelock North
Waipukerau
Eketahuna
Carterton Masterton
Martinborough

Napier

Thames
Huia Lodge Bed & Breakfast
Val and Steve Barnes
Tel: 07 8686557
589 Kauaeranga Valley Road
Thames
Fax: 07 8686557

Single: $35
Double/twin: $70
Breakfast: Cooked
Beds: 2Q 1S
Evening meal: $15pp
Bathrooms: 2EN

Clean comfortable accommodation in picturesque rural setting. Ideal base for Forest Park walks and exploring whole Peninsula. Only 1.5 hours from Auckland City and Airport.

Joy and Sam's Bed & Breakfast
Joy and Sam Arrell
Tel: 07 8689383
111c Grafton Road
Thames
Fax: 07 8686676
Email: samjoy@xtra.co.nz

Single: $45
Double/twin: $60
Breakfast: Special
Beds: 2D
Evening meal: $20pp
Bathrooms: PR

Joy and Sam invite you to stay in their home. Comfort, friendliness and Kiwi hospitality our specialty. We enjoy meeting people. Please request evening meals by 4pm.

Kauaeranga Country Bed & Breakfast
Lyn and Dave Lee
Tel: 07 8686895
Kauaeranga Valley Road, Thames
Fax: 07 8686895

Double/twin: $90

Arrive as strangers - leave us as friends.

Coromandel
Karamana 1872

Virginia and Richard Endean
Tel: 07 8667138
Whangapoua Road, Coromandel
Fax: 07 8667477
Mob: 025 735707
Email: 100400.707@compuserve.com

Single: $110
Double/twin: $110
Breakfast: Continental
Beds: 1K 2Q 2S
Evening meal: $35-50pp
Bathrooms: 4EN

Karamana provides a unique and original Colonial experience. Our Historic Homestead is situated in a quiet rural valley beneath the Coromandel Ranges, a minutes drive from Coromandel township with it's wide variety of local attractions. We are proud to offer friendly, relaxed hospitality and our cuisine, based on local specialties is of the highest standard - a feature of the Karamana experience.

Jacaranda Lodge
Gary and Gayle Bowler
Tel: 07 8668002
3195 Tiki Road, SH 25, Coromandel
Fax: 07 8668002

Double/twin: $75-110

Peaceful rural garden setting, organic, ensuites available, friendly.

Rose Cottage
Irene Pearson
Tel: 07 8667047
75 Pagitt Street, Coromandel

Double/twin: $50

Spacious old villa, walk to town, shops, restaurants.

Whitianga

Benny's Rest B&B
Barbara and Trevor Bennett
Tel: 07 8665464
252 Cook Drive, Whitianga
Fax: 07 8660446

Double/twin: $70-80

Your satisfaction is our pleasure. Cat & small dog.

Cosy Cat Cottage
Gordon Pearce
Tel: 07 8664488
41 South Highway
Whitianga
Fax: 07 8664488

Single: $50-60
Double/twin: $80-90
Breakfast: Special
Beds: 2Q 1D 1S
Evening meal: Not available
Bathrooms: 2EN 1PR

Welcome to our picturesque cottage. Enjoy the amusing catty décor and unique feline ambience! Delicious complimentary breakfasts, comfortable guest lounge. Friendly helpful service. Town centre 1km.

The Beach House Bed & Breakfast
Helen and Allan Watson
Tel: 07 8665647
38 Buffalo Beach Road, Whitianga
Fax: 07 8665647
Mob: 025 2847240
Email: swatson@ww.co.nz

Single: $50-150
Double/twin: $80-150
Breakfast: Cooked
Beds: 1K 1Q 3S
Evening meal: Not available
Bathrooms: 2EN 1PR

Unequalled location on the beachfront. New spacious upstairs rooms, individual - refrigerators, TV, tea/coffee facilities. Short level walk to waterfront cafes, wharf, ferry and shopping village.

Tairua

The Esplanade Holiday Apartment
John and Sheila Charlton
Tel: 07 8648997
18 The Esplanade, Tairua
Fax: 07 8648997
Email: jcharlton@wave.co.nz

Single: $50-95
Double/twin: $50-95
Breakfast: Continental
Beds: 1D 2S
Evening meal: Not available
Bathrooms: 1EN 1PR

Self contained accommodation providing discerning comfort for up to 4 persons. Beautiful waterfront setting, modern fully equipped kitchen, washing machine, drier, garage private garden area.

Whangamata

Brenton Lodge
Jan and Paul Campbell
Tel: 07 8658400
1 Brenton Place, Whangamata
Fax: 07 8658400
Mob: 025 780134

Double/twin: $195

Charming guest cottages. Peace, privacy, pampering, sea views.

Bushland Park Lodge & Nickel Strausse
Reinhard and Petra Nickel
Tel: 07 8657468
444 Wentworth Valley Road
Whangamata
Fax: 07 8657486
Email: bushparklodge@xtra.co.nz

NEW ZEALAND TOURISM AWARDS FINALIST 1998

Single: $100-140
Double/twin: $125-160
Breakfast: Special
Beds: 3Q
Evening meal: From $25pp
Bathrooms: 3EN

Take a break in Whangamata's rainforest and unique bush retreat with authentic German Black Forest restaurant. Accommodation & dining under one roof will give you total relaxation.

Tukere House B & B
Maureen Halligan
Tel: 07 8658009
124 Tukere Drive
Whangamata
Fax: 07 8658009

Single: $45-55
Double/twin: $75-95
Breakfast: Cooked
Beds: 1Q 3S
Evening meal: $15-25pp
Bathrooms: 1EN 1GS 1FS

2kms Northside, shops, beach. Peaceful on edge of Upper Harbour.

Waihi
Riverside

Thea Mosch   David Parish
Tel 07 8636205
17 Riverbank Terrace, Waihi
Fax 07 8636205
Mob 021 612992
Email dparish@xtra.co.nz

Single: $45
Double/twin: $60
Breakfast: Continental
Beds: 2S
Evening meal: $15pp
Bathrooms: 1EN

Located on the edge of the township, 'Riverside' enjoys a rural outlook and seclusion and yet is a mere ten minute stroll from the business centre of Waihi. All guests are welcome to relax in our spa pool and so rest their weary travellers limbs. The guest area is totally self contained with a small dining room-lounge and kitchen area with a microwave oven so that visitors can feel free to prepare their own light meals should that be desired. We regard ourselves as relatively seasoned travellers and enjoy nothing more than swapping experiences with folk from within New Zealand or from other lands. For the sports lovers we would be delighted to arrange a game of golf or tennis, a spot of fishing (trout or snapper) or a bush walk for you. Note: Alternative phone number 07 8638780.
Directions: Just before you leave Waihi and head towards Tauranga take the last turning to the right into Adams St, turn left into Rosemont Rd and left again into Riverbank Tce. 'Riverside' is the last house in the road.

Spindrift Beachstay
Loretta Austin
Tel: 07 8635136
287 Seaforth Road, Waihi Beach
Fax: 07 8635136
Mob: 025 2781887

Double/twin: $75

Surf and harbour beaches, walking, golf(1 1/2), thermal pools.

Waterfront Homestay
John and Kay Morgan
Tel: 07 8634342
17 The Esplanade, Waihi Beach
Fax: 07 8634342
Mob: 025 2871104
Email: k.morgan@xtra.co.nz

Single: $70-90
Double/twin: $70-90
Breakfast: Continental
Beds: 1Q 1D 1S
Evening meal: Not available
Bathrooms: 1PR

Spacious self contained unit on ocean beach waterfront. Two bedroomed accommodation with own entrance exclusively for guest use. Breakfast includes fresh bread. Restaurants nearby.

West Wind Gardens B&B
Josie and Bob French
Tel: 07 8637208
22 Roycroft Street

Double/twin: $60

Enjoy a warm welcome and spectacular gardens.

Katikati
Peaceful Panorama Lodge
Heather and Bernie Wills
Tel: 07 5491882
901 SH2, Katikati,
 Bay of Plenty
Fax: 07 5491882
Email: wills@bopis.co.nz

Single: $45
Double/twin: $75-95
Breakfast: Special
Beds: 2D 3S
Evening meal: $20pp
Bathrooms: 1EN 1GS

A pleasant surprise: delicious home-made meals, sea views, pool. 10 acres with orchard, poultry, cows and birds. No cats or dogs, smoke-free, easy to find.

Properties are listed North to South where possible within regions.

Matamata
Southern Belle Bed and Breakfast

Leanne and Mal
Tel: 07 8886804
101 Firth St, Matamata
Fax: 07 8886824
Free: 0800 244 233
Email: southernbelle@xtra.co.nz

Single: $50
Double/twin: $60-70
Breakfast: Extra $4-10pp
Beds: 1D 3S
Evening meal: $15-25pp
Bathrooms: 1GS

This stately home built in 1936 has been transformed to elegant, luxurious accommodation for the discerning traveller. The separate upper storey guest wing is completely self-contained and includes sunny guest lounge with refrigerator, tea/coffee making facilities, TV, stereo, sparkling bathroom and separate toilet. Only five guests are accommodated per night guaranteeing privacy in a homely welcoming atmosphere. Room-service breakfasts - other meals by arrangement. Free pick-up from train/bus stations or a leisurely two hour drive from Auckland. Matamata boasts many attractions including racecourse, museum, hot springs, 18 hole golf course, gliding and skydiving, interesting boutiques, specialist shops, restaurants and cafes to suit all tastes. Two minute walk to shops. Tours available include garden safaris, canoe adventures, deer parks, horse studs, Maori Marae visits, arts/crafts and 22 walking tracks.
Southern Belle has an in-house clinic where Mal practices Clinical Hypnotherapy - a unique experience for guests.

Whitewood

Bruce and Anne Topless
Tel: 07 8885651
Taihoa North Road
Matamata
Fax: 07 8885621

Single: $70
Double/twin: $100
Breakfast: Continental
Beds: 1Q 1D 4S
Evening meal: $25pp
Bathrooms: 1PR 1GS

Bruce and Ann welcome you to Whitewood, situated 3km from Matamata on the Tauranga Highway - 80mins from Auckland. A large country home offering sophisticated hospitality, set in extensive gardens with magnificient views of the Waikato. Swimming pool, barbeque, sauna and lawn tennis court provide the guest with entertainment and relaxation. Six golf courses, hot pools, clay bird shooting and tramping are nearby. Trout fishing 15 minutes away, with Tauranga and Rotorua within 45 minutes, Waitomo and Taupo 1 1/2 hours drive. Matamata has the largest thoroughbred horse training and stud industry in NZ - tours can be arranged. Guests are welcome to join their hosts for an evening meal, or private dining and lounge facilities are available. It is the aim of Whitewood to provide quality accommodation with that extra special feeling of home.

Wilson Self-contained Farmhouse

Anne Wilson
Tel: 07 8887424
Station Road, RD 2
Matamata
Mob: 025 2780684
Alternative phone number 07 8889383.

Single: $45
Double/twin: $55
Breakfast: Extra $5pp
Beds: 2D 3S
Evening meal: Not available
Bathrooms: 1GS

Self contained 'Early century farmhouse' at 'Northwood', 2 miles from Post Office. Pleasant secluded garden. Farm walks. Less than an hour's drive to Tauranga, Rotorua, Hamilton.

Dream Catcher Country Stay

Sue Giles
Tel: 07 8885508
182 Station Road
Matamata
Mob: 025 802793

Single: $50
Double/twin: $100-150
Breakfast: Cooked
Beds: 2Q 3S
Evening meal: $20pp
Bathrooms: 1EN 1GS

Situated 1/2 km from the Matamata town boundary, 1/2 km off the road in a peaceful rural setting, we are in the beautiful Waikato. Central to all tourist destinations, Golf courses, horse studs, race courses, hot pools, Waharoa Airfield for parachuting, gliding, scenic flights. Relax in our Spa pool.
Note: Please use mobile phone number during business hours.

Tauranga
Taiparoro House 1882

Kevin and Lois Kelly
Tel: 07 5779607
11 5th Avenue, Tauranga
Fax: 07 5779264
Mob: 025 2235675
Email: kl.kelly@clear.net.nz

Single: $95
Double/twin: $135-190
Breakfast: Cooked
Beds: 3Q 1D 2S
Evening meal: Not available
Bathrooms: 5EN

Quality accommodation and memorable hospitality in our lovingly restored Victorian villa amidst tranquil surroundings overlooking Tauranga Harbour.

Highlands Homestay
Shirley and John Whiteman Double/twin: $75
Tel: 07 5525275
89 Whakamarama Road, Tauranga

Privacy assured. Spectacular views. 15 mins. To Tauranga.

Hollies Homestay
Shirley and Michael Creak Double/twin: $110-150
Tel: 07 5779678
Westridge Drive, Tauranga
Fax: 07 5791678
Mob: 025 2767195
Email: hollies@clear.net.nz

Elegant spacious country house - relax in the garden or pool.

Leach Homestay
Kath and Vic Leach Single: $30
Tel: 07 5443514 Double/twin: $50
171B Maungatapu Road
Tauranga

Matua Bed & Breakfast
Peter and Anne Seaton Double/twin: $75
Tel: 07 5768083
34 Tainui Street, Matua
Tauranga

Enjoy private garden in peaceful sunny Matua home.

Pukemapu Homestead
John and Jill Mitchinson Single: $65
Tel: 07 5433502 Double/twin: $90
208 Pukemapu Road, Oropi Breakfast: Cooked
Tauranga Beds: 2Q 2S
Fax: 07 5433512 Evening meal: $25pp
Mob: 025 992148 Bathrooms: 1EN 1GS

'Pukemapu Homestead' - beautiful views - quiet country atmosphere. Close to golf club, racecourse, heated swimming pool, and fifteen minutes to Tauranga city or Mt Maunganui beaches.

Mt Maunganui/Papamoa

Fitzgerald's Irish Inn
Bill and Enda Fitzgerald Double/twin: $70-80
Tel: 07 5754013
463 Maunganui Road, Mt Maunganui

Close to sporting fixtures, hot pools, downtown Mount.

Markbeech Homestay
Joan and Jim Francis Single: $35
Tel: 07 5420815 Double/twin: $65
274 Dickson Road, Papamoa Breakfast: Cooked
Mob: 025 318132 Beds: 1D 3S
Free: 0800 168791 Evening meal: $18pp
  Bathrooms: 1GS

Since retirement we have hosted for 10 years and our interests are gardening and travel. A safe bathing beach is 200 metres distant.

Pembroke House

Cathy and Graham Burgess
Tel: 07 5721000
12 Santa Fe Key, Royal Palm Beach,
Papamoa
Email: pembrokehouse@xtra.co.nz

Single: $50
Double/twin: $80
Breakfast: Cooked
Beds: 2Q 2S
Evening meal: Not available
Bathrooms: 1EN 1GS

We welcome guests to our new home with guest lounge. Cross the road to Ocean Beach to enjoy swimming, surfing and beach walks. Smoke free.

Te Puke

Croeso i Hafod

Maureen H Oliver
Tel: 07 5331086
151 Wilson Road South, Paengaroa
Te Puke
Fax: 07 5331086

Single: $40
Double/twin: $75
Breakfast: Continental
Beds: 4S
Evening meal: $20pp
Bathrooms: 2EN

Two acre open garden.

Omaranui Orchard

Bruce and Marie Stephens
Tel: 07 5737842
716 Rangiuru Road
Te Puke

Single: $45
Double/twin: $75
Breakfast: Continental
Beds: 1K 2S
Evening meal: $20pp
Bathrooms: 1GS

Bruce and Marie, Kiwifruit orchardists, offer comfortable home with attractive garden and hearty meals. For your enjoyment - golf course nearby sea and troutfishing arranged on request. Smoke free home.

Whakatane/Ohope

Harbour View

Peter and Beryl Carter
Tel: 07 3124441
122A Harbour Road, Ohope, Bay of Plenty

Double/twin: $65

Harbours Edge, holiday flat, Ocean Beach 5 min walk.

Henton's Bed & Breakfast

Marion and Graham Henton
Tel: 07 3125095
295 Pohutukawa Avenue,
Ohope Beach, Bay of Plenty
Fax: 07 3125095

Single: $50-70
Double/twin: $70-90
Breakfast: Continental
Beds: 1D
Evening meal: $20pp
Bathrooms: 1PR

Spacious, modern guest suite. Self contained. TV, video, microwave, private courtyard, BBQ available. Situated 150m from beach. Handy to Licensed Chartered Club, Cafes, bowls, golf.

Travellers Rest

Jeff and Karen Winterson
Tel: 07 3071015
28 Henderson Street,
Whakatane

Double/twin: $70

Welcome to our peaceful environment and accommodation.

Opotiki
Fantail Cottage
Colin and Beryl Jobson
Tel: 07 3154981
318 Ohiwa Harbour Road
Bay of Plenty
Fax: 07 3154981

Single: $45
Double/twin: $70
Breakfast: Continental
Beds: 1Q 2S
Evening meal: Not available
Bathrooms: 1EN 1GS

A friendly welcome awaits you in tranquil surroundings rich in history. Enjoy panoramic views, fishing, swimming, rare birds and outdoor spa overlooking harbour and sea.

St Johns Cottage
Diane Monteith
Tel: 07 3156645
Cnr Ford & St John Street, Opotiki

Double/twin: $80

1920's two storey cottage in 1/2 acre garden.

Te Kaha Guest House
Maida and David Glasgow
Tel: 07 3252009
6646 SH 35, Te Kaha, Oporiki
Bay of Plenty
Fax: 07 3252004
Email: davidmaida@xtra.co.nz

Single: $45
Double/twin: $70
Breakfast: Continental
Beds: 2Q 1D 4S
Evening meal: $25pp
Bathrooms: 1EN 1GS

Ideal stopover on the Pacific Coast Highway to fish, boat, swim dive, or just relax and enjoy the spectacular coastal scenery and mediterranean climate.

Tolaga Bay
Willowflat Farmstay
June and Allan Hall
Tel: 06 8626341
Mangatuna, Tolaga Bay
Fax: 06 8626371

Double/twin: $65

Walkways, horses, piano, spa pool, fishing in summer.

Gisborne
Glen Innis Farm Stay/B&B
The McDonald family
Tel: 06 8637127
Hangaroa
Gisborne

Single: $35
Double/twin: $70
Breakfast: Cooked
Beds: 4S
Evening meal: $15pp
Bathrooms: 1FS

Share with us comfortable shearers quarters beside tranquil trout river opposite Hangaroa bluffs. Hill country sheep and cattle station with day to day farming operations. If no reply Ph 06 8637126.

Rouse Beach Stay
Dot and Peter Rouse
Tel: 06 8688111
111 Wairere Road, Wainui Beach, Gisborne
Fax: 06 8688162

Double/twin: $80

Situated on beachfront 5km out of Gisborne.

Studio 4 Bed and Breakfast

Judy and Gavin Smith
Tel: 06 8681571
4 Heta Road
Gisborne
Fax: 06 8681457

Single: $50
Double/twin: $70
Breakfast: Continental
Beds: 1Q 3S
Evening meal: $20pp
Bathrooms: 1PR 1GS

Studio 4 is 8 mins walk to the City, museum and wharf area. We offer off-street parking in peaceful surroundings backing on to a park and river. Original artworks can be viewed or purchased from our small gallery. We welcome you to a pleasant stay in Gisborne.

Tararau

Harry and Helen Stott
Tel: 06 8628660
2053 Wharerata Road,
Muriwai
Gisborne

Single: $85
Double/twin: $110
Breakfast: Cooked
Beds: 1Q
Evening meal: $25pp
Bathrooms: 1EN

Spend some time at Tararau cottage by the river, we are in a rural setting. A game dinner can be prepared if requested, depending on the season as to what is available with complimentary wine or springwater home brew. Morere Hot Springs and bush walks are within close distance as is the splendid Eastwood Hill Abritorian. We look forward to meeting you and sharing our country lifestyle.

Seaview Natural Healing Centre
Norman and Diana Weiss Double/twin: $60
Tel: 06 8672790
32 Douglas Street, Okitu Beach, Gisborne
Email: normyw@hotmail.com

Peaceful setting minutes from beach. Healing sessions available.

Mahia
Beachfront Homestay
David and Alan Double/twin: $80
Tel: 06 8375705
7 Moana Drive, Mahia Beach, Hawkes Bay
Fax: 06 8375705
Email: BeachfrontHomestay@xtra.co.nz

Dinner available. Spectacular location.

Braeside Bed & Breakfast
Kaye and Ron Fisher Double/twin: $55
Tel: 06 8375742
Mahanga Beach Road, Mahia Peninsula, Hawkes Bay
Fax: 06 8375745

Sunrise and sea views. Private grounds. Country hospitality.

Tunanui Station Cottages
Ray and Leslie Thompson Double/twin: $120-150
Tel: 06 8375790
Tunanui Road, Opoutama, Hawkes Bay
Fax: 06 8375797
Mob: 025 2402421

Fine self contained accommodation, panoramic views, tennis, horse-riding, river-swimming. Additional guests $25. Breakfast extra $12pp.

Wairoa
Waiatai Valley Farm Stays

Sophia and John Ross Single: $125
Tel: 06 8377552 Double/twin: $125
Pirinoa Station, 418 Waiatai Valley Road Breakfast: Special
Wairoa, Hawkes Bay Beds: 1K 1D 1S
Fax: 06 8377409 Evening meal: $35pp
 Bathrooms: 1FS

Self-contained cottage on 520 hectare sheep and cattle farm. Explore local bush walks and farmland for spectacular views of Hawkes Bay. Handy to Mahia Peninsula for fishing and swimming and Morere Hot Springs. Relax on the verandah watching the sunset, treating yourself to one of Sophia's gourmet meals.

Riverside Homestay
Cherry Metz **Double/twin:** $60
Tel: 06 8387346
48 Kopu Road, Wairoa
Hawkes Bay

Riverside walks to beach or town. Quiet location.

Waiata Farm
David and Gay Withers **Double/twin:** $65
Tel: 06 8383858
196 Awamate Road, Wairoa
Hawkes Bay
Fax: 06 8383858

Comfortable home 6 minutes from Wairoa. Evening meal extra.

Lake Waikaremoana
9 Rotten Row Homestay

Judy Doyle **Single:** $40
Tel: 06 8373701 **Double/twin:** $70
9 Rotten Row, Tuia **Breakfast:** Cooked
via Wairoa **Beds:** 1Q 2S
Hawkes Bay **Evening meal:** $20pp
  Bathrooms: 1FS

Lake Waikaremoana National Park trout fishing - bushwalking-boating, canoeing,paradise. Tuai Hydro-Electricity Village is the gateway to this unique wilderness area. I offer you a quality homestay experience in my comfortable modernised bungalow (circo 1928) overlooking peaceful Lake Whakamarino Reserve, 10 mins from Lake Waikaremoana.

Remember, evening meals are by arrangement only unless the property has its own restaurant.

Napier
Cornucopia Lodge

Kees Peters   Joss Lamers
Tel: 06 8366508
361-363 SH 5, Eskdale
Napier
Fax: 06 8366518
Email: cornucopia@clear.net.nz

Single: $150
Double/twin: $165-250
Breakfast: Special
Beds: 1Q 1D
Evening meal: $69pp
Bathrooms: 2EN

The perfect place for 2-4 guests in selfcontained cottage set on a 3 acre property with fruit and nut trees overlooking vineyards and enjoying unsurpassed hospitality.

No 11

Phyllida and Bryan Isles
Tel: 06 8344372
11 Sealy Road
Napier
Mob: 025 2463968

Single: $50
Double/twin: $90
Breakfast: Special
Beds: 1Q 2S
Evening meal: Not available
Bathrooms: 1GS

The name says it all! 11/10 for comfort, convenience and conviviality. Comfort - New villa with views and spacious, sunny quality rooms. TV, tea-making facilities. Convenience - easy walk to city, cafes, Ahuriri and Napier's attractions. Drive or bus to wineries, gannets. Conviviality - warm welcome and everything to make your stay enjoyable.

Spence Homestay

Kay and Stewart Spence
Tel: 06 8359454
17 Cobden Road
Napier
Fax: 06 8359454

Single: $55
Double/twin: $85
Beds: 2Q 2S
Evening meal: Not available
Bathrooms: 2EN

Early colonial 1880 sunny home pleasantly situated in large attractive grounds which include petanque court. 10 to 15 minutes walk to art deco city centre. Guest rooms are spacious with ensuites, comfortable lounge chairs, tea making facilities and TV. Close to wineries and gannet sanctuary.

Deco Dreams
Vernon and Kathie
Tel: 06 8446685
Tom Parker Avenue, Marewa, Napier
Fax: 06 8446685
Mob: 021 688085
Email: vnapier@clear.net.nz

Single: $160
Double/twin: $160-200
Breakfast: Special
Beds: 1D 2S
Evening meal: Not available
Bathrooms: 1PR

Enjoy the privacy and amenities of a stand-alone Art Deco home furnished in the 30's style. Close to Napier City centre and Hawkes Bay attractions.

France House
Nett and Russell Buchanan
Tel: 06 8367035
Shaw Road (SH 5), Eskdale, Hawkes Bay
Fax: 06 8367035

Double/twin: $80

Historic ex-orphanage offering traditional homestead style accommodation.

Sea Breeze Bed & Breakfast
Huia Te Kanawa   Mike Fogarty
Tel: 06 8358067
281 Marine Parade, Napier
Fax: 06 8350512

Double/twin: $75

Central beachfront location, Art Deco, pacific rim cuisine, wineries.

The "Large" House
Judith and John Double/twin: $155-165
Tel: 06 8350000
4 Hadfield Terrace, Napier
Fax: 06 8352244
Mob: 025 2452870
Email: large@xtra.co.nz
Internet: friars.co.nz/hosts/largehouse.html

Historic - private - romantic - idyllic

Turangi Bed & Breakfast
Joan and David Donaldson Double/twin: $90
Tel: 06 8357795
1 Hukarere Road, Bluff Hill, Napier
Fax: 06 8357096

Queen suite, sea views, access parking, near city.

Hastings
Hawthorne Country House

Jeanette and Peter Kelly
Tel: 06 8780035
420 SH2, Hastings
Fax: 06 8780035
Mob: 025 413755
Email: hawthorne@xtra.co.nz

Single: $140
Double/twin: $165
Breakfast: Cooked
Beds: 4Q 1D 1S
Evening meal: $35pp
Bathrooms: 5EN

Hawthorne is a gracious Edwardian villa, rich with the elegance of a bygone era, yet providing all the modern comforts of a boutique bed and breakfast. Each of the five individually furnished guest rooms has an ensuite bathroom and opens onto deep verandahs, leading directly into the expansive country garden.

Coldora Rural Homestay
Colin and Dorothy Ashton Double/twin: $80
Tel: 06 8775177
393 Middle Road, Pukahu, Hastings

Modern, spacious, vast tranquil views, children & handicapped welcome.

Lancewoods
Pat and Alf Macdonald
Tel: 06 8783370
604 Whitehead Road, Hastings

Continental breakfast, scenic parks, wine tra

McConchie Homestay
Doug and Barbara McConchie
Tel: 06 8784576
115A Frederick Street, Hastings

Friendly hosts. No animals. Attractive, quiet, central city.

Phillips Homestay
Ros Phillips   **Double/twin:** $60
Tel: 06 8774111
Middle Road, Havelock North
Fax: 06 8774111

Space. Peace. Good food. Dinner on request.

Raureka
Rosemary and Tim Ormond   **Single:** $60
Tel: 06 8789715   **Double:** $70
26 Wellwood Road, RD 5   **Breakfast:** Cooked
Hastings   **Beds:** 1Q
Fax: 06 8789715   **Bathrooms:** 1EN

3 kms to town centre. Separate unit from house. Quiet no exit road. Close to golf courses and boutique wineries. Tennis court and swimming pool onsite.

Waipukurau

Porongahau Lodge
Winton Hall   **Double/twin:** $68-89
Tel: 06 8555386
Porangahau, Central Hawkes Bay
Fax: 06 8555386

Beach, sun, swim, fish, golf, relax, gin, party.

Eketahuna

Putara Valley Farmstay
Eunice and Byron Algie   **Double/twin:** $50
Tel: 06 3758535
Putara, Eketahuna

Self-contained cottage.
Hunting, trout fishing, horse riding, farm activities.

Masterton

Kummerstein
Kevin and Dawn Beange   **Double/twin:** $75
Tel: 06 3727005
Kaiwhata Road, Tewharau
Fax: 06 3727005

Farmstay 50kms east of Masterton. Peaceful relaxation close to coast.

...les

...eve Blakemore Double/twin: $80
...2577
...ohiwi Road, Homebush, Masterton
06 3772578

Tranquil French farmhouse - petanque, river, wildfowl - dinner available.

Tidsfordriv Country Homestay
Glenys Hansen Double/twin: $65
Tel: 06 3789967
Cootes Road, Matahiwi, Masterton
Fax: 06 3789957

Parklike surroundings, wetlands and birdlife, 64 acre farmlet.

Willowgrove Farmstay
Elaine and Arthur Dew
Tel: 06 3774627
Homebush,
Masterton
Fax: 06 3773617
Internet:
www.wairarapa.co.nz/accommodation

Single: $35
Double/twin: $75
Breakfast: Cooked
Beds: 1K 2S
Evening meal: $15pp
Bathrooms: 1FS

Refurbished 1900 villa, large gardens. Small farm breeding cattle & sheep. Shearing & dog demonstrations. River boundary for trout fishing, swimming. 3 km from Masterton.

Carterton
Galtimore
Kerry and Mary Ann Maher
Tel: 06 3796616
Kokotau Road, RD 2 Ponatahi
Carterton
Free: 0800 770001

Single: $95
Double/twin: $95
Breakfast: Continental
Beds: 1Q
Evening meal: Not available
Bathrooms: 1EN

Take a break and unwind in our well appointed "log cabin." Private and tranquil setting a short stroll across paddock to the Ruamahanga river.

Martinborough
The Martinborough Connection

Margaret Coney
Tel: 06 3069708
80 Jellicoe Street
Martinborough
Mob: 025 371773

Single: $110-120
Double/twin: $110-120
Breakfast: Special
Beds: 4Q
Evening meal: Not available
Bathrooms: 4EN

Originally built in the 1880's The Martinborough Connection is a beautifully restored country-style weekend bed and breakfast guesthouse with four guest rooms (each with ensuite) which all open on to a verandah and lawn. There is also a guest lounge'dining area with an open fireplace. Rooms available by prior booking only. (Not really suitable for children.)
Rooms available during the week - block bookings only.

WAIKATO/TARANAKI/WANGANUI/MANAWATU/HOROWHENUA/WELLINGTON

Te Kauwhata
Huntly
Raglan
Hamilton
Cambridge
Otorohanga
Te Kuiti
Piopio
Waitara
New Plymouth
Stratford
Hawera
Hunterville
Wanganui
Marton
Fielding
Levin
Palmerston North
Otaki
Waikanae
Wellington

Te Kuiti

Te Kauwhata
Herons Ridge Farmstay

David Sharland
Tel: 07 8264646
1131 Waikare Road,
Te Kauwhata
Fax: 07 8264646

Single: $50-70
Double/twin: $80-120
Breakfast: Cooked
Beds: 2Q 1D 1S
Evening meal: $25pp
Bathrooms: 1EN 1PR

Luxurious garden studio or in-house garden suite.
Our KiwiHost farmstay set in 25 acres close to Lake Waikare is 1 hour south of Auckland.

Huntly
Parnassus Farm & Garden

David and Sharon Payne
Tel: 07 8288781
Te Ohaki Road, Huntly
Fax: 07 8288781
Email: parnassus@xtra.co.nz

Double/twin: $70

Rural tranquility, superb food, only minutes off SH 1

Raglan
Rangimaarie Seaside Retreat

Carolyn Evans
Tel: 07 8257567
78G Moonlight Bay, Greenslade Road, Raglan
Fax: 07 8257566

Double/twin: $60/75

Spectacular views, private beach, spa pool, homebaked fare.

Hamilton
The Monastery

Diana and Robert Scott
Tel: 07 8569587
212B Newell Road, Hamilton
Fax: 07 8569512

Single: $100
Double/twin: $130
Breakfast: Cooked
Beds: 2D 4S
Evening meal: $40pp
Bathrooms: 2EN 1GS

This historic home offers Edwardian elegance in a peaceful rural setting near the Waikato River. Two large lounges feature open fires, antiques, kauri panelling, pressed steel ceilings and stained glass windows. Attractive comfortable bedrooms have fresh flowers and port. Enjoy special breakfasts, warm hospitality and relaxing garden and river walks.

Green Gables of Rukuhia

Earl and Judi McWhirter
Tel: 07 8438511
35 Rukuhia Road, RD 2, Ohaupo
Fax: 07 8438514
Ohaupo
Email: judi@stats.waikato.ac.nz

Single: $45
Double/twin: $75
Breakfast: Continental
Beds: 2D 3S
Evening meal: $20pp
Bathrooms: 1GS

Quiet rural location. 5 minutes to Hamilton and Hamilton airport (courtesy car). Fresh home-baked bread and selection of coffees to suit.

Ridge House

Kay and John Bates
Tel: 07 8236555
15 Main Road, Ohaupo
Fax: 07 8236555

Double/twin: $60

Warm hospitality, lovely pastoral views, central. Ideal base.

Cambridge
Birches Farmhouse B & B

Sheri Mitchell   Hugh Jellie
Tel: 07 8276556
Maungatautari Road, Pukekura, Cambridge
Fax: 07 8273552 Mob: 025 882216

Double/twin: $85

Elkayel Stables

John Congdon
Tel: 07 8272765
Oreipunga Road
Fax: 07 8272737

Single: $45
Double/twin: $75
Breakfast: Cooked
Beds: 4S
Evening meal: $20pp
Bathrooms: 1GS

Lovely cape-cod house set in the scenic Waikato Valley farmland with superb views over the Waikato River. Adjacent to the largest horse training establishment in New Zealand for interested parties to investigate. Trout fishing, glow worm and evening BBQ tours available.

Riverlands

Deborah Evans   Dave Lamb
Tel: 07 8276730
7 Pope Terrace, Cambridge
Fax: 07 8391627

Double/twin: $70

Cosy comfortable home stay in 'Town of Trees'. Dinner available.

Otorohanga
Brake's B & B

Ernest and Ann Brake
Tel: 07 8737734
147 Main North Road, SH 3, Otorohanga
Mob: 025 845419

Double/twin: $70

18 kms from Waitomo Caves.

Meadowland Farmstay B&B

Tony and Jill Webber
Tel: 07 8737729
746 SH 31, RD 3
Otorhanga
Fax: 07 8737719

Single: $45-50
Double/twin: $65-75
Breakfast: Cooked
Beds: 1Q 3D 2S
Evening meal: Not available
Bathrooms: 1EN 1GS

Tony and Jill invite you to see their panoramic views of farmland, Otorohanga Kiwi house and Waitomo Caves. Self contained unit, swimming pool, tennis court.

Te Kuiti
Proffit Farmstay

Lyn and Jeff Proffit
Tel: 07 8787572
Troopers Road, Te Kuiti
Fax: 07 8787573

Double/twin: $70

Handy to Waitomo. Farm tours. Cave. Lovely views.

Piopio
Edenridge

Ron and Heather Barclay
Tel: 07 8778881
Piopio
Fax: 07 8778881
Email: barclay@waicomp.co.nz

Single: $80
Double/twin: $80
Breakfast: Continental
Beds: 1Q 2S
Evening meal: From $25
Bathrooms: 1GS

Welcome to the lush green of Northern King Country - relax or fish the many trout streams at our back door. World shearing capital. Guides provided for; Farm tours, bush walks, hunting, diving, sea fishing, golf or visit Waitomo Caves. Large new pleasant farm style living area. Dinners, lunches available. (Smokers welcome)

Waitara
Sea King Homestay

Mary and Layton King
Tel: 06 7547207
135 Turangi Road, Motunui, Waitara

Double/twin: $70-80

Unique, seaside, rural, comfortable. Spectacular views. Coastal walks.

New Plymouth
Alice Jane House

Sue and Andrew Weir
Tel: 06 7581440
60 Pendarves Street
New Plymouth
Fax: 06 7581430
Mob: 025 737095

Single: $55
Double/twin: $75
Breakfast: Cooked
Beds: 1K 1Q 3S
Evening meal: Not available
Bathrooms: 1GS

This charming sunny central city villa has been renovated and refurbished with top quality furnishings. Two guest lounges enable the choice of enjoying the warmth of the log fire in winter in the formal lounge or relaxing in the TV lounge. Each bedroom has its own character and ambience reflecting the charm of yesteryear. Crisp white linen, luxurious towels and fresh flowers guarantees a memorable start to your stay. A welcoming cup of tea or cappuccino/expresso coffee, where each cup is freshly ground, always awaits you. Breakfasts consist of continental, traditional or a special delight to tantalise your tastebuds. Just minutes walk from the city's beautiful westcoast shorefront,
restaurants, shops and Art Galleries. Heritage walkways surround us and the renowned Pukekura Park and Bowl of Brooklands are just around the corner. Spectacular Mount Egmont/Taranaki is just 30 minutes drive for those keen trampers and skiers.

Balconies Bed and Breakfast

Trevor and Vivien Lewis
Tel: 06 7578866
161 Powderham Street
New Plymouth
Fax: 06 7599366
Mob: 025 423789

Single: $50
Double/twin: $70
Breakfast: Special
Beds: 3Q 2S
Evening meal: Not available
Bathrooms: 1GS

Located just 500 metres (5 min walk) from the New Plymouth shopping centre. Our comfortable 110 year old character manor is set in lovely garden surrounds and offers three downstairs tastefully decorated guest rooms, large guest bathroom, separate toilet and spacious guest lounge with tea and coffee facilities.
Off street parking, courtesy transport.

Kirkstall B&B

Lindy MacDiarmid   Ian Hay
Tel: 06 7583222
8 Baring Terrace
New Plymouth
Fax: 06 7583224

Single: $50
Double/twin: $70
Breakfast: Cooked
Beds: 1Q 2D 1S
Evening meal: $25pp
Bathrooms: 2GS

Our 1920's character home is set amongst a cottage garden, sloping from street level to the river below. Is open to the public during the Taranaki Rhododendron Festival (Oct/Nov). The house is full of character with open fires during the winter and great views to Mt Egmont. 200m to the beach and walkways.
A warm welcome is assured.

Birdhaven

Ann and John Butler
Tel: 06 7510432
26 Pararewa Drive, New Plymouth
Fax: 06 7513475
Free: 0800 306449

Single: $50-60
Double/twin: $72-80
Breakfast: Special
Beds: 1Q 2S
Evening meal: $30pp
Bathrooms: 1GS

Your comfort and pleasure is important to us. Share the tranquility of our spacious home overlooking native bush, birdlife and the woodland surroundings of our farmlet.

Forrestal Lodge

Chip and Margaret Rangi
Tel: 06 7567242
23 Rimu Street, Inglewood

Double/twin: $55

Peaceful, homely, affordable, central to all tourist attractions.

Mountain Dew Farmstay

Marion and Geoff Rivers
Tel: 06 7535123
1602 Carrington Road, New Plymouth
Email: m_g.rivers@clear.net.nz

Double/twin: $75

Large, quiet, views, sc kitchen, bath, adults, upstairs.

Powell Homestay

Claire and Mick Powell
Tel: 06 7586462
26 Tokomaru Street, New Plymouth

Double/twin: $60

Ranui Bed & Breakfast

Tom and Joan Johnston
Tel: 06 7588204
341 St Aubyn Street, New Plymouth
Email: ranui@netsource.co.nz

Double/twin: $50

Overseas and Kiwi guests say we're incredible value.

Stratford

Anderson's Alpine Residence

Keith and Berta Anderson
Tel: 06 7656620
922 Pembroke Road, Stratford
Fax: 06 7656100
Mob: 025 412372
Free: 0800 668682
Email: mountainhouse@xtra.co.nz.

Single: $95-120
Double/twin: $95-120
Breakfast: Cooked
Beds: 1K 1D 2S
Evening meal: Not available
Bathrooms: 3EN

Proud of our three storied Swiss Chalet set in native garden and bush opposite Egmont national park. Panoramic alpine views. Pet sheep, duck, pig etc. Note: Evening meals available at Mountain House $30pp. Internet: www.mountainhouse.co.nz

Neilds B&B / Farmstay

Joy and Bill Neild
Tel: 06 7655927
299 Cardiff Road, Stratford

Single: $30
Double/twin: $60

Hawera
Bradley Homestay

Noeline and Eddie Bradley
Tel: 06 2728206
1 Wynyard Street, Normanby
Hawera

Single: $35
Double/twin: $70
Breakfast: Cooked
Beds: 1D 1S
Evening meal: $20pp
Bathrooms: 1GS

Our home is 5 kilometers north of Hawera, just off SH 3 in a semi-rural area, peaceful and quiet although handy to town, restaurants, etc. Hawera's a farming center with an excellent museum, several fine bowling greens, golf courses, racecourse, etc. We are semi-retired farmers, know the district well and really enjoy visitors.

Rowe Homestay

Ian and Diana Rowe
Tel: 06 2784037
110 Turuturu Road, Hawera

Single: $40
Double: $55
Children: $20

Wanganui
Riverside Inn

Joy and Philip Gedye
Tel: 06 3472529
2 Plymouth Street
Wanganui
Fax: 06 3472529

Single: $45
Double/twin: $70
Breakfast: Continental
Beds: 4D 8S
Evening meal: Not available
Bathrooms: 3GS

Our homestead, built in 1895, has been restored to retain its "old world charm" of how New Zealand used to be. Guest rooms are located on ground floor. Laundry and fully euipped self service kitchen are available. We can ensure you a comfortable stay in a smoke-free environment.

Crellow House

Pam Noyes
Tel: 06 3450740
274 Taupo Quay
Wanganui

Single: $35
Double/twin: $60
Breakfast: Special
Beds: 1D 4S
Evening meal: $15pp
Bathrooms: 1EN 1GS

Unique, historuc, century-old home beside the Wanganui River. Comfort assured. Nothing too much trouble. Courtresy car to bus/plane. Generous home-cooked dinner by arrangement. Pets OK.

The Flying Fox

Annette Main   John Blythe
Tel: 06 3428160
Right Bank Whanganui River, Koriniti
Wanganui
Fax: 06 3428160
Mob: 025 400483
Email: tourism@wanganui.govt.nz

Single: $45
Double/twin: $70
Breakfast: Special
Beds: 2D 2S
Evening meal: $25pp
Bathrooms: 1GS

This unusual property is accessible only by aerial cableway or by boat. Secluded accommodation with interesting outdoor bathing options. Advance bookings necessary to ensure access.

Hunterville
Brick n' Birches

Shona and John Kilsby
Tel: 06 3228442
48 Ongo Road, Hunterville
Fax: 06 3228442
Mob: 025 2798890

Single: $60
Double/twin: $100-110
Breakfast: Cooked
Beds: 1K 4S
Evening meal: $25pp
Bathrooms: 3EN

Just two minutes from SH 1 midway between Taupo and Wellington, we offer friendly hospitality in our character two storied home. Don't miss a memorable experience.

Marton
Dunollie

Melva McDougall
Tel: 06 3276771
Bonny Glen
Marton

Single: $30
Double/twin: $60
Breakfast: Cooked
Beds: 1D 2S
Evening meal: $20pp
Bathrooms: 1FS

Welcome to Dunollie my home. We built 40 years ago, 5 minutes from Marton, 20 minutes from Wanganui. My interests are gardens, pottery, weaving and travel. I have a cat and 12 red hens.

Tataramoa Bed & Breakfast Farmstay

Janice and Des Gower
Tel: 06 3278778
Howie Road, Marton

Double/twin: $80

140 year old colonial homestead amongst bush and gardens.

Feilding
Puketawa
Nelson and Phyllis Whitelock
Tel: 06 3287819
Colyton Road
Fielding
Fax: 06 3287919

Single: $40
Double/twin: $70
Breakfast: Cooked
Beds: 1Q 2S
Evening meal: $25pp
Bathrooms: 1GS

Discover tranquility in the unique surroundings of Puketawa - ten acres of native bush and beautiful gardens. National award winning home. Country hospitality at its best.

Walker Homestay
Beryl Walker
Tel: 06 3234409
5 Wellington Street,
Feilding

Double/twin: $60-70

Centrally placed Bed & Breakfast in friendly atmosphere.

'Rather see the wonders of the world abroad than, living dully sluggardized at home, wear out thy youth with shapeless idleness.' - **Shakespeare**

Palmerston North
Contact House

Colin and Penny Stichbury
Tel: 06 3553653
186 Fitzherbert Avenue
Palmerston North
Fax: 06 3553687
Mob: 025 718889
Email: contact.house@clear.net.nz

家

Single: $55-65
Double/twin: $85-95
Breakfast: Cooked
Beds: 6Q 9D 3S
Evening meal: $12-20pp
Bathrooms: 2EN 1PR 1GS

'Potato and Rice', a mix of two cultures. When the Kowhai tree at the rear of our property flowers, Tui's soon arrive to sip the nectar and sing their song of thanks and gratitude. Guests at Contact House, like the Tui, love the yellow, blues and greens of our décor, colours chosen by Colin's gracious Taiwanese wife Penny. The nectar on offer at Contact House is delicious Taiwanese food. Coffee, tea and hot chocolate are free and in all rooms. The food Penny cooks is home made and authentic. It is an expression of Penny's gratitude for being accepted warmly and careingly into a new culture. By sharing her food it is Pennys way of saying thankyou Palmerston North and New Zealand, welcome all to 'Penny's Wok' and Contact House.
- Hygienic bathrooms with disposable toilet seat protectors.
- 'Penny's Wok' open Friday and Saturday nights BYO licence.
- Close to Massey University, College of Education, sports grounds, city center shopping, supermarkets, night clubs, restaurants (Fishermans Table & Amarda Carvery), tennis courts, swimming pool, rose garden.
- Late checkout.
- Study desks.

The Gables Bed and Breakfast

Paul and Monica Stichbury
Tel: 06 3583209
179 Fitzherbert Avenue
Palmerston North
Fax: 06 3583209
Mob: 021 2142588

Single: $60-80
Double/twin: $80-110
Breakfast: Continental
Beds: 3Q 3S
Evening meal: $15pp
Bathrooms: 1EN 2GS

10 minute walk to the C.B.D. 2 minutes to the nearest restaurant. The Gables is a classic fully restored 1930's home with hotel style rooms. The jewel in the crown is the private apartment behind the house popular with honeymooners, tourists and business people. We can meet public transport.

Clairemont

Dick and Joy Archer
Tel: 06 3575508
20 Snowdon Avenue
Palmerston North

Single: $40
Twin: $65
Breakfast: Cooked
Beds: 3S
Evening meal: Not available
Bathrooms: 1FS

We are in a quiet area near the river, walkways and golf course, not far to shops. Private lounge if requested. Reps welcome.

Glenfyne

Jill and Alex McRobert
Tel: 06 3581626
413 Albert Street, Hokowhitu
Palmerston North
Fax: 06 3581626

Double/twin: $70

Close to Massey University, town and golf course.

Iti Mara Homestay

Dixie and Neil Signal
Tel: 06 3542666
3 Peters Avenue
Palmerston North
Fax: 06 3542666

Single: $50
Double/twin: $70
Breakfast: Extra charge
Beds: 1D 2S
Evening meal: $20pp
Bathrooms: 1EN

Private, sunny, self contained one double bedroom flat with two divan beds in spacious living area. Off road carport, Laundry. Extra persons $15. Non smoking inside. Cooked breakfast $5pp.

Levin
Lily's B&B / Homestay
Mary and Dennis Robinson
Tel: 06 3689536
335 Foxton Road, Levin
Fax: 06 3689536 Email: lilysbnb@xtra.co.nz

Double/twin: Enquire

Seventy mins to/from ferry - rural setting.

Otaki
Aotaki Homestead
Judy and Paul Allen
Tel: 06 3646438
11 Dunstan Street, Otaki
Fax: 06 3646461

Double/twin: $75

Magic hidden setting just off SH1. Simple access.

Clulee-McKewen Pear Farm
Robin Clulee   Lois McKewen
Tel: 06 3642063
101 School Road, Te Horo
Email: r.f.clulee@xtra.co.nz

Double/twin: $90

Excludes school holidays. Tranquil environment and great food.

Glenmore
Jack and Heather Bellaney
Tel: 06 3647319
Rahui Road, Otaki
Fax: 06 3647797

Double/twin: $65

Tranquil garden setting, great views. Wellington 55 mins.

Waikanae
Waikanae Beach Homestay
Pauline and Allan Jones
Tel: 04 2936532
115 Tutere Street, Waikanae Beach
Fax: 04 2936543
Mob: 025 300785

Double/twin: $75

Comfortable home, direct access to sandy swimming beach.

Wellington
Eight Parliament Street
Christine Voelker
Tel: 04 4990808
8 Parliament Street, Thorndon
Wellington
Fax: 04 4796705
Mob: 025 2806739
Email: grasenack@xtra.co.nz

Single: $95
Double/twin: $118-140
Breakfast: Special
Beds: 3Q
Evening meal: Not available
Bathrooms: 1EN 1GS

Whether you are a traveler or on business our B&B offers you a stylish, comfortable and central base (whole house rental possible) to explore Wellington's attractions. Internet: www.webnz.co.nz/8parliament

The Posthouse

Martin and Jenifer Thomas
Tel: 04 3857707
22 Cleveland Street, Brooklyn
Wellington
Fax: 04 3857727
Mob: 025 959975
Email: reservations@theposthouse.co.nz

Single: $185
Double/twin: $200
Breakfast: Special
Beds: 1Q
Evening meal: Enquire
Bathrooms: 1EN

Located in a quiet street just five minutes from central Wellington, The Posthouse was constructed in 1914 as the Brooklyn Post Office and has now been restored and decorated in the grand style of the 1920's. Guest accommodation comprises just one lavishly decorated suite, separate from the main house, with its' own private entrance and ensuite bathroom featuring an Edwardian bath and basin. Creature comforts include imported linens and antique Italian bedspreads, handmade soaps and luxurious toiletries, a midnight snackbox of various delicacies and truffles, flowers fresh from the garden and refreshments served to your room according to whim. French doors open to a terrace for dining in the garden. Breakfast can be delivered to your room or enjoyed upstairs in the main house. In keeping with the Thomas' love of good food and their history as restauranteurs breakfast has more than just a touch of glamour. To start the day try freshly pressed juices, cinnamon buns straight from the oven, bircher muesli with fresh berries, coconut waffles layered with tropical fruit and maple cream, grilled foccacia with field mushrooms, free range scrambled eggs and fresh herbs - accompanied by enormous mugs of café latte or a pot of fragrant tea. Private dining by special arrangement. The Posthouse - unsurpassed in Wellington for private accommodation. EFTPOS and major credit cards accepted. Internet: www.theposthouse.co.nz

The Lighthouse

Bruce and Rosemary Stokell
Tel: 04 4724177
326 The Esplanade, Island Bay
Wellington
Fax: 04 4724177
Mob: 025 425555
Email: bruce@sportwork.co.nz

Single: $150-180
Double/twin: $150-180
Beds: 1D
Evening meal: Not available
Bathrooms: 1PR

Self contained, great views, warm, close to town. Note: Ingredients provided to prepare own breakfast. Local restaurants and takeaway food closeby.

Tinakori Lodge

Mel and John Ainsworth
Tel: 04 4733478
182 Tinakori Road, Thorndon
Wellington
Fax: 04 4725554
Email: 100035.3214@compuserve.com

Single: $70-85
Double/twin: $95-120
Breakfast: Special
Beds: 3K 3Q 6S
Evening meal: Not available
Bathrooms: 5EN 2GS

Tasteful accommodation conveniently situated in historic Thorndon, a short walk to city features, Botanic Gardens, restaurants etc. Scrumptions breakfast buffet.

Newton Homestay

K P Heggie   C P Marmont
Tel: 04 3890416
85 Rintoul Street, Newtown, Wellington

Double/twin: $79+

Superior Victorian villa, quiet, views, on bus route.

Korokoro Homestay

James and Bridget Austin
Tel: 04 5891678
100 Korokoro Road, Korokoro
Petone, Wellington
Fax: 04 5891678
Email: jaustin@clear.net.nz

Single: $45
Double/twin: $75
Breakfast: Continental
Beds: 1D 2S
Evening meal: $30pp
Bathrooms: 1GS

Spacious bedrooms, very quiet. Our peaceful property has large country-style garden, harbour views, convenient, 12 mins to ferry and Wellington, easily found. Non-smoking.

Ngaio Homestay

Brian and Jennifer Timmings
Tel: 04 4795325
56 Fox Street, Ngaio, Wellington
Fax: 04 4794325
Mob: 025 2769437
Email: jennifertimmings@clear.net.nz

Single: $60
Double/twin: $85-95
Breakfast: Continental
Beds: 2D 3S
Evening meal: $20pp
Bathrooms: 3EN 1PR

We offer good quality quiet comfortable smoke-free accommodation, 3km to ferry, 7km to central Wellington. One Ensuite ($85) and two S/C ($95) apartments, perfect for business or holiday travellers.

Plimmerton Homestay

Cren and Rae Collins
Tel: 04 2331367
12 Roys Road, Plimmerton, Wellington

Double/twin: $50

Comfortable, homely. Great view. Ensuite bathroom. Please phone.

Te Marua Homestay

Sheryl and Lloyd Homer
Tel: 04 5267851
108A Plateau Road, Te Marua, Upper Hutt
Fax: 04 5267866
Mob: 025 501679
Email: sheryl.lloyd@clear.net.nz
Free: 0800 110851

Double/twin: $70

Private, peaceful bush setting. Fishing, golf, outdoor bath.

The Mermaid (Guesthouse for women)

F. Brice
Tel: 04 3844511
1 Epuni Street, Wellington
Fax: 04 3844511
Mob: 025 2265108
Email: mermaid@sans.vuw.ac.nz

Double/twin: $68

Historic Central City suburb, elegantly decorated, luscious breakfast.

Treetops

Robyn and Roger Cooper
Tel: 04 5627692
7 Huia Road, Days Bay, Wellington
Fax: 04 5627690
Email: r.cooper@gns.cri.nz

Double/twin: $85

Self-contained, warm, spacious bush hideaway with private cablecar.

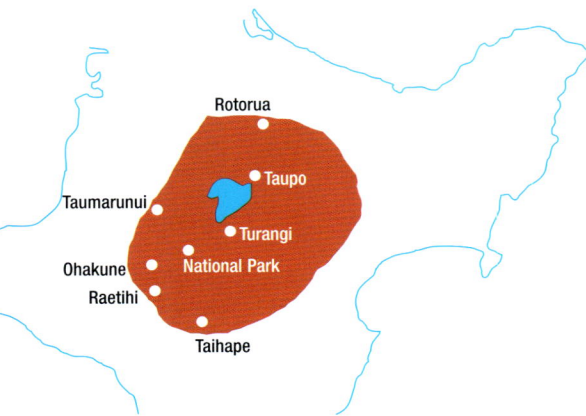

Rotorua
Clover Downs Estate

Lyn and Lloyd Ferris
Tel: 07 3322366
175 Jackson Road, RD 2
Rotorua
Fax: 07 3322367
Mob: 025 712866
Email: ferris@cloverdowns.co.nz

Single: $115-140
Double/twin: $125-150
Breakfast: Special
Beds: 2K 1Q
Evening meal: $45pp
Bathrooms: 3EN

So country yet so close to town, only 15 minutes drive. Affordable luxury farm accommodation with total commitment to comfort, quality and high standards, ensuring you of a memorable stay. CLOVER DOWNS ESTATE is situated on a secluded 35-acre quality assurance accredited Deer and Ostrich farm overlooking Lake Rotorua. Three beautifully appointed spacious bedrooms are each equipped with Sky TV, fridge, tea & coffee facilities and private ensuite complete with toiletries, hairdryer and bathrobes. Take a farm tour on our 4WD bike with Lloyd and the dogs, try a game of Petanque or relax in the hot tub. With extensive overseas and New Zealand travel experience, we can gladly help in arranging bookings for Rotorua attractions and activities as well as assisting you with onward travel plans.
Warm welcome, traditional hospitality and wonderful experience await you at CLOVER DOWNS ESTATE. Directions please telephone, E-mail, fax or write for bookings and directions.

Alrae's Lakeview Homestay
Alf and Raema　　　　　　　　　Double/twin: $85-95
Tel: 07 3574913
124 Leonard Road, Ngongotaha
Rotorua
Fax: 07 3574913
Mob: 025 2750113
Free: 0800 270943
Email: alraes@xtra.co.nz

With the million dollar view over Lake Rotorua

Brinkler Farmstay
Enid and John Brinkler　　　　　Double/twin: $70
Tel: 07 3323306
89 Fryer Road, Ngongotaha
Rotorua

Comfortable farmhouse; magnificent lakeviews; tourism attractions close proximity.

Chalfont Heights Bed & Breakfast Farmstay
Annie Wells　　　　　　　　　　**Single:** $50
Tel: 07 3572014　　　　　　　　　**Double/twin:** $75
Rotorua　　　　　　　　　　　　　**Breakfast:** Special
Fax: 07 3572014　　　　　　　　　**Beds:** 1K 1Q 4S
Mob: 025 595157　　　　　　　　　**Evening meal:** $30pp
　　　　　　　　　　　　　　　　　Bathrooms: 1PR

Annie invites you to her piece of heaven! 8 ks Rotorua city. Garden, farm, lake views from every room. Farm tour Red deer, Belted Galloway cattle.

Eaton Hall
Colin and Maureen Brown　　　　Double/twin: $75-80
Tel: 07 3470366
1255 Hinemaru Street, Rotorua
Fax: 07 3470366
Free: 0800 328664

Close by to Polynesian spa and orchid garden.

Inner City Homestay
Irvine and Susan Munro　　　　　Double/twin: $75
Tel: 07 3488594
1126 Whakaue Street, Rotorua

Spacious parkside home 200 metres tourism convention centres.

Te Ana Farmstay
Heather and Brian Oberer　　　　Double/twin: $90
Tel: 07 3332720
Poutakataka Road, Ngakuru, Rotorua
Fax: 07 3332720
Mob: 025 828151

Taupo
Catley's Homestay

Tom and Beverley Catley
Tel: 07 3781403
55 Grace Crescent
Taupo
Fax: 07 3781402

Single: $50
Double/twin: $80-90
Breakfast: Cooked
Beds: 1Q 1D 2S
Evening meal: $20pp
Bathrooms: 1PR 2FS

We warmly welcome you to our sunny spacious home and colourful garden. Upstairs bedrooms open onto a sheltered sundeck with extensive views of lake and mountains. Downstairs accommodation consists of a bedroom, lounge and kitchenette with its own garden entrance. Laundry facilities are available and your satisfaction is our priority.

Ridgeview Deer Farm

Raewyn and Barry Wyllie
Tel: 07 3789469
1062 Mapara Road
Taupo
Fax: 07 3770710
Mob: 025 948682
Email: ridgevw@voyager.co.nz

Single: $60
Double/twin: $100
Breakfast: Cooked
Beds: 1K 1D 2S
Evening meal: $25pp
Bathrooms: 1EN 1GS

Welcome to our 80 hectare property, which is situated 15 minutes from Taupo and farms elk and red deer. Our modern homestead, set in three acres of landscaped gardens, has a 360 panaromic view of Lake Taupo and the mountains of the Tongariro National Park, tranquil countryside and Taupo township.

190 Spa Rd
Ron and Anne Bickers Double/twin: $70
Tel: 07 3770665
190 Spa Road, Taupo

Ensuite. Sunny. Beautiful view over Waikato river.

A Majestic Hideaway
Noeline Anderson   Martin Hulsdouw Double/twin: $80
Tel: 07 3772393
67 Koha Road, Taupo
Fax: 07 3772393
Mob: 025 767639
Email: majestic@imail.org

Majestic views, homely. Privacy and quietness abounds. Central location.

Ben Lomond
Jack and Mary Weston Double/twin: $90
Tel: 07 3776033
1434 Poihipi Road, Taupo
Fax: 07 3776033
Mob: 025 774080

Comfortable country homestay on 500 acre sheep farm.

Brackenhurst
Margaret and Noel Marson Double/twin: $90
Tel: 07 3776451
801 Oruanui Road, Taupo
Fax: 07 3776451

Tranquil farmstay just off highway one.

Jensen Homestay
Patricia and Russell Jensen **Single:** $65
Tel: 07 3781888 **Double/twin:** $95
5 Te Hepera St, **Breakfast:** Cooked
Taupo **Beds:** 1Q
Fax: 07 3781888 **Evening meal:** $35pp
 Bathrooms: 1PR

Sunny home on quiet cul-de-sac offering panoramic views. Close to lake and town. Accommodation is upstairs level including guest lounge with balcony. Private thermal pool.

Richlyn
Lyn and Richard James Double/twin: $88-131
Tel: 07 3788023
1 Mark Wynd, Bonshaw Park
Taupo
Fax: 07 3788023
Mob: 025 908647

Seven acres, gardens, views, gym, spa pool, sleeps eight.

Riverway Cottages

Joyce and John Johnson
Tel: 07 3788822
16 Peehi Manini Road
Waitahanui
Taupo
Mob: 025 2781732

Single: $45
Double/twin: $75
Breakfast: Continental
Beds: 1Q 1D 1S
Evening meal: Enquire
Bathrooms: 1GS

Riverway Cottage is two bedroomed self-contained accommodation walking distance to river and lake. John is a fly fishing guide and can show you some magic places.

South Claragh

Lesley and Paul Hill
Tel: 07 3728848
State Highway 32
Taupo
Fax: 07 3728047
Email: paul.hill@xtra.co.nz

Single: $45-55
Double/twin: $90
Breakfast: Cooked
Beds: 1Q 1S
Evening meal: $30pp
Bathrooms: 1PR

Turn into our leafy driveway and relax. Comfortable farmhouse in rambling garden with donkeys and coloured sheep. Your hosts - well travelled, semi retired professional people with varied interests. Note: Cottage also available (sleeps 2-5).

Twynham at Kinloch

Eliza Whitelock
Tel: 07 3782862
84 Marina Terrace, Kinloch
Taupo
Fax: 07 3782868
Mob: 025 2856001

Double/twin: $115

Delightful lakeside village, 15 mins Taupo, tranquil home and garden, pets welcome.

Villa Don Quixote

Erik Velthuis
Tel: 07 3773941
122 Oruanui Road, Taupo
Fax: 07 3773941

Double/twin: $90-100

Comfortable country homestay situated just 9km from Taupo

Remember, evening meals are by arrangement only unless the property has its own restaurant.

Turangi
River Birches

Peter and Gill Osborne
Tel: 07 3865348
21 Koura Street
Turangi
Fax: 07 3865948
Email: gillo@voyager.co.nz

Single: $95
Double/twin: $150
Breakfast: Special
Beds: 1K 2S
Evening meal: Not available
Bathrooms: 1PR

Set in tranquil gardens on the banks of the Tongariro River this cottage is the perfect hideaway. An attractive, homely atmosphere, pot-belly, heaters. Electric blankets ensure your comfort. A delicious breakfast is left to eat at your leisure. Stay hidden away or wander over to share a chat, coffee or wine. Note: King bed can convert to two singles.

Akepiro

John and Jenny Wilcox
Tel: 07 3867384
169 Taupahi Road, Turangi
Fax: 07 3866838
Email: jwilcox@voyager.co.nz

Double/twin: $65

A home from home, ideal retreat, set in own garden, direct access Tongariro.

Taumarunui
Walker Farmstay

Yvonne and Eric Walker
Tel: 07 8966041
Waituhi
Taumarunui
Fax: 07 8966040

Single: $35
Double/twin: $60-70
Breakfast: Cooked
Beds: 1D 2S
Evening meal: $15pp
Bathrooms: 1FS

We invite you to spend time with us on our 360 hectare sheep and beef farm in the peaceful Waituhi Valley 20 minutes from Taumarunui.

National Park
Pukenui Lodge

Chris and Natalie
Tel: 07 8922882
Millar Street, National Park Township
Fax: 07 8922900
Mob: 021 892288
Free: 0800 785368

Single: $35-45
Double/twin: $60-85
Breakfast: Cooked
Beds: 6D 2S
Evening meal: $17.50pp
Bathrooms: 8GS

Natalie and Chris welcome you to come and enjoy this winter/summer playground situated in the heart of the Wanganui and Tongariro National Parks. Quad rooms also available.

Ohakune
Rimu Park Lodge and Chalets

Phil Abel
Tel: 06 3859023
27 Rimu Street
Ohakune
Fax: 06 3859023

Single: $55-85
Double/twin: $75-95
Breakfast: Continental
Beds: 6D 6S
Evening meal: Not available
Bathrooms: 4EN 1GS

It is immediately evident on arrival at Rimu Park Lodge that this is no sterile motel. The vintage 1934 railway carriage that greets you as you drive in and the beautiful 1914 villa set the scene for a charming and homely stay. A nice spacious lawn, well established gardens and trees and great views to the park and snowy Mt Ruapehu (from your pillow in the carriage) makes it a pretty and relaxing spot. The carriage has been beautifully restored featuring lovely wood paneling, red velvet curtains and a beautiful tile and brass bathroom. There's original rail seats at your dining table, a fridge, toaster, jug for you to prepare our continental breakfast at your convenience. The TV's in the cupboard so you can imagine you're back in the 30's.

A unique and charming experience. 300m from the mountain road; a spectacular sealed road through rain forest, then through ancient dwarfed beech trees to Turoa Skifield. Walks from 20 min to 5 hours. Stunning views to Mt Taranaki and the south western North Island. Also 2 more conventional studio units, 4, 6 and 10 berth self contained chalets or inexpensive family or multishare rooms in the lodge. Kitchen facilities may be available.
Note: Cooked breakfast available in ski season.
Walking distance to restaurants.

Mitredale Farmstay
Audrey and Diane Pritt Double/twin: $70
Tel: 06 3858016
Smiths Road, Ohakune
Fax: 06 3858016

Comfortable, friendly with great views, pets and tasty food.

Raetihi
Robb Farmstay
Ken and Sonia Robb Double/twin: $70
Tel: 06 3854581
Pipiriki Road, Raetihi
Fax: 06 3854581

1000 acres farming sheep and cattle. Mountain views.

Taihape
Papa Pottery and B&B
Lindsay and Cathy Baine Double/twin: $65
Tel: 06 3880318
24 Huia Street, Taihape
Fax: 06 3880318

A great place to stop. Friendly and comfortable.

Tarata Fishaway - Fishingstay/Farmstay
Stephen and Trudi Mattock Double/twin: $110
Tel: 06 3880354
5251 Mokai Road, Taihape
Fax: 06 3880954

A Rangitikei river holiday 'right at your doorstep'.

Notes :

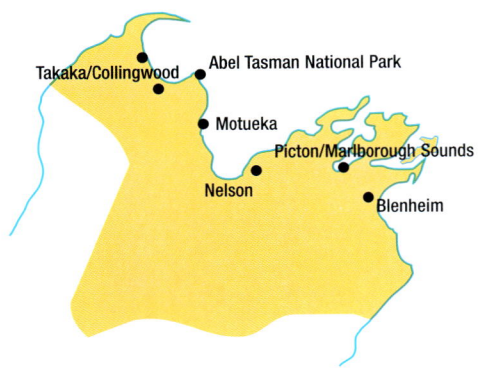

Takaka Hill

Takaka/Collingwood
Amanzi
Barbara and John Dunn **Double/twin:** $75
Tel: 03 5259615
Rangihaeata Road, Takaka
Fax: 03 5259678

Self-contained unit, private, peaceful, spectacular coastal views.

Golden Bay Homestays
Philip Langford **Double/twin:** $50/80
Tel: 03 5259593
Glendale, Dodsons Road, Takaka

Skara Brae
Jan and John Wilson-Riddell **Single:** $50
Tel: 03 5248464 **Double/twin:** $60-75
Elizabeth Street **Breakfast:** Continental
Collingwood **Beds:** 3D 2S
Evening meal: Not available
Bathrooms: 2EN 1FS

Situated in the heart of Collingwood. Kahurangi National Park: Farewell Spit Nature Reserve: Whangauni Marine Reserve: and the Heaphy Track. Collingwood has it all!

Abel Tasman National Park
Abel Tasman Marahau Lodge

Jan Caird **Single:** $108-136
Tel: 03 5278250 **Double/twin:** $108-136
Marahau Beach, Motueka **Breakfast:** Cooked
Fax: 03 5278258 **Beds:** 3K 4Q 12S
Email: marahau.lodge@clear.net.nz **Evening meal:** $30pp
Bathrooms: 8EN

Abel Tasman Marahau Lodge is just a five minute walk from Abel Tasman National Park, water taxis, sea kayaking, horse trekking and the Park Café. The Lodge is located in a peaceful natural setting with facilities such as room service meals, spa and sauna and on-licence. A great get-away from it all.

The Beach House
Shirley Ryan **Double/twin:** $55
Tel: 03 5280040
Lagoon Street, Torrent Bay
Abel Tasman National Park
Fax: 03 5476674

Comfort - beauty - in the heart of the park. Note: Postal address c/- Ryan, 39 Coster St, Nelson.

Motueka
Hillview Bed 'n' Breakfast

John and Pauline Westall
Tel: 03 5289909
527 Main Road, Riwaka
RD 3 Motueka
Fax: 03 5289919

Single: $40
Double/twin: $70-85
Breakfast: Continental
Beds: 1Q 1D 2S
Evening meal: Not available
Bathrooms: 1EN 1GS

We welcome guests to our relaxed, smoke free home situated on SH60, 5 minutes from Motueka. We are close to the Motueka river, renown for its trout fishing, approximately 15 minutes from Kaiteriteri beach and Marahau, gateway to the Abel Tasman National Park with activities such as kayaking, llama treks and tramping.

The Maples Bed & Breakfast

Maya Mosimann   Ruedi Kappeli
Tel: 03 5432008
Harakeke
Upper Moutere
Fax: 03 5432008

Single: $55
Double/twin: $85-95
Breakfast: Special
Beds: 3K
Evening meal: $25pp
Bathrooms: 1GS

Relax on the verandah or play badminton in our delightful parklike garden. This interior designer's home offers beautifully decorated bedrooms with comfortable beds and a luxuriously fitted rimu-bathroom. Our delicious breakfasts include homemade swiss fruit muesli, breads, croissants, jams and espresso coffee. Tasty evening meals always available.

The
TRI-ANGLE INN B&B

Motueka, New Zealand

Tri-angle Inn Bed & Breakfast

Lesley and Daniel Jackson
Tel: 03 5287756
142 Thorp Street, Motueka
Mob: 025 484778
Email: Daniel.hdt@xtra.co.nz

Single: $55
Double/twin: $95
Breakfast: Special
Beds: 2Q 2S
Evening meal: Not available
Bathrooms: 2EN

A warm welcome will be found at the Tri-Angle Inn, we aim to offer comfort at affordable prices in a stress free semi-rural setting. Our rooms are large and comfortable, each has its own private entrance and en-suite. Have a wonderful holiday experience with us here in Mot.

Copper Beech Gallery

John and Carol Gatenby
Tel: 03 5287456
240 Thorp Street
Motueka
Fax: 03 5287456

Single: $90
Double/twin: $130
Breakfast: Special
Beds: 1Q 2S
Evening meal: Not available
Bathrooms: 2EN

We are all you require for the perfect holiday. Friendly ambience, two acre garden, rural and tidal outlook, two minutes to town, artists haven, onsite gallery, painting tuition available.

Doone Cottage Country Homestay

Stan and Glen Davenport   **Double/twin:** $110-130
Tel: 03 5268740
Motueka Valley Highway, Motueka
Fax: 03 5268740
Mob: 021 707055
Double/twin: $110-130
Old homestead. Large garden. Animals. Weaving. Trout fishing.

Kairuru Farm Stay

David and Wendy Henderson   **Double/twin:** $100
Tel: 03 5288091
SH 60, Takaka Hill
Fax: 03 5288091
Mob: 025 337457
Email: kairuru@xtra.co.nz

Working sheep/cattle farm, 3 private cottages.

Motueka Homestay
Ian and Rebecca Williams
Tel: 03 5289385
184 Thorp Street, Motueka
Fax: 03 5289385

Single: $30
Double/twin: $60
Breakfast: Continental
Beds: 1Q 1D 3S
Evening meal: $20pp
Bathrooms: 1EN 1FS

Ian and Rebecca invite you to spend time with us. Upstairs is lounge, bedroom, ensuite. Below is double room and swimming pool.

The Birches
KJ & M Burrows
Tel: 03 5289950
216 Thorp Street,
Motueka

Single: $55
Double/twin: $90
Breakfast: Continental
Beds: 1Q 1D
Evening meal: Not available
Bathrooms: 1GS

Spend quality time in the dress circle of Motueka, gateway to Abel Tasman and Kahurangi national parks, fishing, tramping, sea kayaking, wine and craft trails.

Nelson

Glendora "Wisteria Cottage"

Shona and Hugh Moon-Gordon
Tel: 03 5418813
Wai-iti, Wakefield, Nelson
Fax: 03 5418826
Email: wisteria@glendora.co.nz

Single: $90
Double/twin: $110
Breakfast: Special
Beds: 1Q 2S
Evening meal: $25pp
Bathrooms: 1EN

Self contained 'Rural Retreat'. Garden setting offers Peace, Privacy and Comfort. Studio plan, decorated with flair and imagination. Log fire, electric blankets, heated towel rails, hair dryer, shaver-point, laundry facilities. Self-catering option. Life-style farmlet in the beautiful Wai-iti valley. Nelson 25 minutes, award winning restaurants 15minutes. We are "smoke free." Note: Tariff for extra adults $35pp.

Abbey Lodge
Carol and Warren Carey
Tel: 03 5488816
84 Grove Street, Nelson
Fax: 03 5484220

Double/twin: $68

Good budget accommodation. Walking distance to city, family atmosphere.

Almond Cottage
Tom and Janet Jones
Tel: 03 5479486
3/60 Songer Street,
Stoke, Nelson

Single: $55
Double/twin: $70
Breakfast: Special
Beds: 1D 2S
Evening meal: $20pp
Bathrooms: 1GS

"Private, secluded, peaceful. Homemade bread, yoghurt included with breakfast, is served on our garden patio.
500 metres to sea walks, old English pub and restaurant."

Althorpe
Bob and Jenny Worley
Tel: 03 5448117
13 Dorset Street, Richmond, Nelson
Fax: 03 5448117   Free: 0800 ALTHORPE
Email: rworley@voyager.co.nz

Double/twin: $90-120

'tis Althorpe that beckons the weary traveller'.

Anderson Homestay
Jean and Jack Anderson
Tel: 03 5442175
46 Rochfort Drive, Richmond, Nelson
Fax: 03 5442175

Double/twin: $55

We are happy to meet planes or buses.

Arapiki
Kay and Geoff Gudsell
Tel: 03 5473741
21 Arapiki Road, Stoke, Nelson
Fax: 03 5473742   Mob: 025 517131
Email: arapiki@nelson.planet.org.nz

Double/twin: $65-75

Immaculate smokefree self-contained units. Quiet central location. Continental breakfast $5pp.

Atholwood Country Accommodation
Robyn and Grahame Williams
Tel: 03 5402925
Bronte Road East, Upper Moutere
Nelson
Fax: 03 5402925
Mob: 025 310309

Single: $100-120
Double/twin: $120-135
Breakfast: Special
Beds: 2Q 1S
Evening meal: $35pp
Bathrooms: 2EN

Beauty, seclusion and tranquility is assured within two acres of mature gardens - situated on the shoreline of the waimea inlet. Relax and enjoy.

Cathedral Inn
Jim and Suzie Tohill
Tel: 03 5487369
369 Trafalgar Street South, Nelson
Fax: 03 5480369   Free: 0800 883377
Email: cathedral.inn@clear.net.nz

Double/twin: $145-190

Nelson city's premiere luxury accommodation. Historic character and charm.

Harakeke Lodge
Joan Roesch
Tel: 03 5432799
Harley Road, Upper Moutere, Nelson
Fax: 03 5432799
Email: henry.roesch@clear.net.nz
Note: Queen/ensuite $65
Single with FS bathroom $35

Double/twin: $65

Kershaw House
Ashley and Deidre Marshall
Tel: 03 5440957
10 Wensley Road, Richmond
Nelson
Fax: 03 5440950
Mob: 025 389347

Single: $125
Double/twin: $145-165
Breakfast: Cooked
Beds: 1K 2Q
Evening meal: Not available
Bathrooms: 3EN

Gateway to Nelsons many attractions. Kershaw House is an elegant (1929) home with comfortable lounge and spacious bedrooms. 5 minute walk to shopping centre and award winning restaurants.

Mike & Noelene's Place
Michael and Noelene Smith
Tel: 03 5447279
39 Washbourn Drive, Richmond, Nelson
Fax: 03 5447279
Email: c.pengelly@xtra.co.nz

Double/twin: $80-95

Lovely modern comfortable home. Many attractions close by.

Tarata Homestay
John and Mercia Hoskin
Tel: 03 5473426
5 Tarata Street, Stoke, Nelson
Fax: 03 5473640
Mob: 025 378308
Free: 0800 107308

Double/twin: $65

Quiet location, off-street parking and comfortable guest lounge.

The Wheelhouse Inn
Ralph Hetzel
Tel: 03 5468391
41 Whitby Road, Nelson
Fax: 03 5468391
Mob: 025 493380

Single: $80-95
Double/twin: $80-95
Breakfast: Continental
Beds: 1Q 1D 2S
Evening meal: Not available
Bathrooms: 1PR

A new separate, totally self-contained, multi-level accommodation enjoying spectacular views of sparkling Tasman Bay. Spacious, tastefully decorated and quiet, only 5 minutes from city centre. Breakfast available on request.

Waters Edge
Bernice Stott
Tel: 03 5478324
100 Point Road, Monaco, Nelson
Fax: 03 5478324 Mob: 021 613532
Email: 2bstottberbar.com.nz@clear.net.nz

Double/twin: $60

Waterfront position. Superb sea and mountain views.

Picton/Marlborough Sounds
Colonial House

Susan Cummings
Tel: 03 5737740
133 Waikawa Road
Picton
Fax: 03 5737749

Single: $40
Double/twin: $50-65
Breakfast: Continental
Beds: 1D 3S
Evening meal: Not available
Bathrooms: 1EN 1GS 1FS

Enjoy free tea, coffee and biscuits anytime. Colonial House is handy to the town centre as well as marine and scenic walks. There is off-street parking for both cars and trailers. If you require transport from the ferry please telephone upon arrival. There are both ensuite and share bathroom facilities. And a single rate of $40 applies.

Admirals Lodge B & B Hotel
Lyn and Dick Holmes
Tel: 03 5736590
22 Waikawa Road, Picton
Fax: 03 5738318
Email: admiralb&b@xtra.co.nz

Double/twin: $85

View our Web "Home Page" http://nz.com/Southis/Picton/Admirals

Echo Lodge
Lyn and Eddie Thoroughgood
Tel: 03 5736367
5 Rutland Street
Picton
Fax: 03 5736387

Single: $40
Double/twin: $75
Breakfast: Special
Beds: 1D 3S
Evening meal: Not available
Bathrooms: 2EN 1GS

Welcome to Echo Lodge. Enjoy our special cooked breakfasts in our dining room or on our patio. 5mins walk to all facilities. Courtesy car.

Grandvue
Russell and Rosalie Mathews
Tel: 03 5738553
19 Otago Street, Picton
Fax: 03 5738556
Email: grandvue-mathews@clear.net.nz

Single: $55
Double/twin: $75
Breakfast: Cooked
Beds: 1Q
Evening meal: Not available
Bathrooms: 1EN

Enjoy spectacular views of Picton harbour and town from tranquil surroundings. Five minutes walk to town centre. Courtesy car from Ferry.

Palm Haven

Peter and Damian Robertson **Double/twin:** $60-75
Tel: 03 5735644
5 Newgate Street, Picton
Fax: 03 5735645
Mob: 025 2750860

Tranquil garden setting, easy walk to town.

Seaview

Pam and John Anders **Double/twin:** $70
Tel: 03 5737783
424 Port Underwood Road, Picton
Fax: 03 5737783

Note: S/C also available $60

The Nikaus Country Garden & Farmstay

Alison and Robin Bowron **Double/twin:** $70-110
Tel: 03 5734432
Waitaria Bay, Kenepuru Sound
Fax: 03 5734432
Mob: 025 544712

Family farm, great views, large garden, friendly animals.

Blenheim

Broomfield

Kaye and Gary Green **Single:** $120
Tel: 03 5728162 **Double/twin:** $120
35 Inkerman Street, **Breakfast:** Special
Renwick, Blenheim **Beds:** 1K
Mob: 025 2261769 **Evening meal:** Not available
  Bathrooms: 1EN

Broomfield is our two storied rammed earth house set beside a nectarine orchard in the heart of Renwick wine country. The bedroom overlooks our formally laid out gardens with an interesting potager. Our garden is very much a feature of our home and guests are most welcome to wander through. Around us within 5-10 minutes 16 wineries (8 with restaurants) plus country gardens and olive grove.

Stonehaven Vineyard

David and Jocelyn Wilson
Tel: 03 5729730
445a Rapaura Road
Blenheim
Fax: 03 5729730
Email: dgwilson@voyager.co.nz

Single: $75-90
Double/twin: $105-120
Breakfast: Continental
Beds: 1K 1Q 1S
Evening meal: Enquire
Bathrooms: 1EN 2PR

Our recently built stone and cedar home and swimming pool are surrounded by gardens and 17 acres of Sauvignon Blank vines. Closeby are some of NZ's most outstanding wineries which we can arrange for you to visit. We have the space, comfort and privacy to make your stay relaxing and memorable.

Beaver Bed and Breakfast
Russel and Jennie Hopkins
Tel: 03 5788401
60 Beaver Road, Blenheim
Fax: 03 35788401
Mob: 021 626151
Email: jhopkins@voyager.co.nz.

Double/twin: $70

Private self-contained unit with large bath and shower.

Devonia
Maurie and Marg Beuth
Tel: 03 5729593
2A Nelson Place
Renwick
Blenheim

Single: $55
Double/twin: $75-85
Breakfast: Cooked
Beds: 1Q 2S
Evening meal: Not available
Bathrooms: 1PR 1GS

A colonial style home in 1/2 acre or lovely private grounds - within "stroll and taste" distance of prestigious vineyards
A warm welcome awaits you at "Devonia".

Four Winds Vineyard Accommodation
Ross and Mary Spicer
Tel: 03 5788881
26 Rowberrys Road,
Blenheim
Fax: 03 5788574
Email: fourwind@voyager.co.nz

Single: $40
Double/twin: $60
Breakfast: Extra $5pp
Beds: 1D 3S
Evening meal: Not available
Bathrooms: 1PR

We invite you to our 2 bedroom self contained cottage on our small vineyard in the country just 3km from P.O. Note: Evening meals sometimes avail - please enquire. Families or 3 adults $80 (extra adults $15pp).

Henry Maxwell's
Ken and Christy
Tel: 03 5788086
28 Henry St
Blenheim
Fax: 03 5788089
Email: b&b@mlb.planet.gen.nz

Single: $45
Double/twin: $70-90
Breakfast: Special
Beds: 2Q 1D 2S
Evening meal: Not available
Bathrooms: 2EN 1GS

Four quiet gracious rooms with TVs. Unique décor of maps / charts. Outdoor spa. Fresh bread / fruit juices. Off-street parking. Two minutes walk to central Restaurants.

Maxwell Pass Farmstay
John and Jean Leslie
Tel: 03 5781941
Maxwell Pass, Blenheim
Fax: 03 5781941

Double/twin: $75

Hill country property with beef cattle. Blenheim 8 km.

Rhododendron Lodge Farm Homestay
Charlie and Audrey Chambers
Tel: 03 5781145
SH 1, St Andrews, Blenheim
Fax: 03 5781145

Double/twin: $70-90

Retirement farm, spacious home, swimming pool, private facilities. Blenheim 1.5km.

Sunnymead Cottage
Lisa Jackson
Tel: 03 5777129
Nelson Highway, Blenheim
Fax: 03 5777129

Double/twin: $130

Self-contained historic cottage: quiet, beautiful, delightful; central to vineyards.

Windmill Farm
Millie Amos
Tel: 03 5777853
908B Main Road, Riverlands
Marlborough
Fax: 03 5777853

Double/twin: $75

Properties are listed North to South where possible within regions.

Notes :

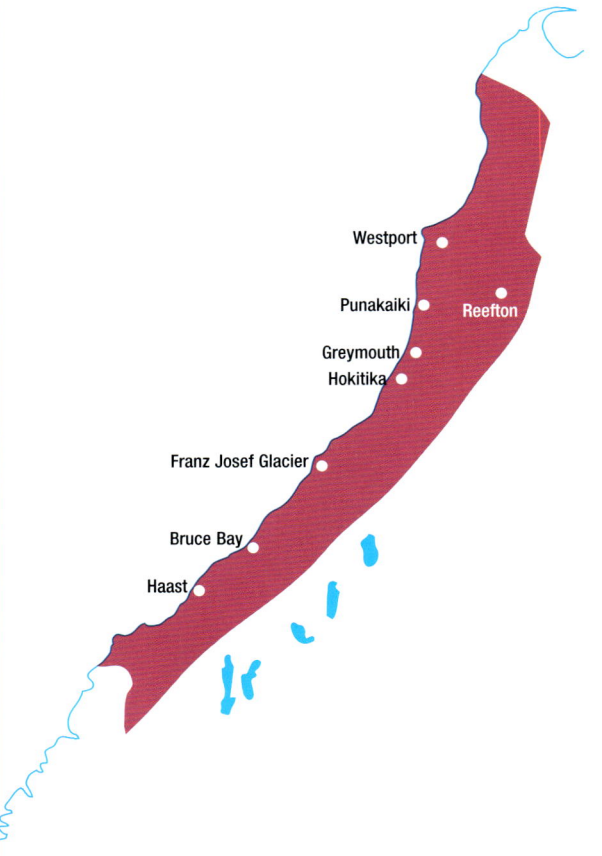

Westport
Beachfront Farmstay
Dianne and Russell Anderson
Tel: 03 7826762
Karamea, Westport
Fax: 03 7826762
Mob: 025 2221755
Email: farmstay@xtra.co.nz

Single: $45
Double/twin: $75
Breakfast: Cooked
Beds: 1D 3S
Evening meal: $20pp
Bathrooms: 1EN 1FS

Come as far north as you can on the West Coast and relax for a few days with tasty home cooking. 2 mins walk to the beach.

Marg's Travellers Rest
Marg Broderick
Tel: 03 7898627
56 Russell Street, Westport
Fax: 03 7898396
Free: 0800 737863

Double/twin: $70

Centrally situated - 'a home away from home'.

River View Lodge
Noeline Biddulph **Double/twin:** $100
Tel: 03 7896037
SH 6, Buller Gorge Road, Westport
Fax: 03 7896037
Free: 0800 184656

New complex overlooking Buller River. Breakfast $7-12pp.

Reefton
Quartz Lodge
Marie and Ray Armstrong
Tel: 03 7328383
78 Sheil Street, Reefton
Fax: 03 7328383
Free: 0800 302725

Single: $30-50
Double/twin: $60-90
Breakfast: Cooked
Beds: 2Q 1D 3S
Evening meal: $20pp
Bathrooms: 2EN 1PR 1GS

Your comfort is our business. Modern two storied lodge, centrally heated. Amazing views from huge windows in all rooms. Only two minute stroll to shops/cafes/bars. Quality queensize beds. Dinners are famous specialising in West Coast produce served in our upstairs lounge/dining room with New Zealand wines and beers. Guests only private area and entrance. Laundry, fax, telephone, local information, newspapers. Separate backpackers accommodation also available.

Reef Cottage Bed & Breakfast Inn
Susan and Ronnie Standfield **Double/twin:** $70-95
Tel: 03 7328440
51 Broadway, Reefton
Fax: 03 7328440
Mob: 025 2264013
Free: 0800 770440
Email: rstandfield@clear.net.nz

Restored historic home, quality and adventure await the discerning traveller.

Punakaiki
Mamaku Lodge
Allan Wilkie   Petra Ingenbleeck
Tel: 03 7311853
Hartmount Place
Punakaiki

Single: $70-80
Double/twin: $80-90
Breakfast: Cooked
Beds: 1D 2S
Evening meal: Not available
Bathrooms: 1PR

Private lodge in forest setting with spectacular sea views. Location 3 km north of Pancake Rocks at blue bed sign. Great walks, guided tours and hot pool.

Punakaiki Cottage Motels
Stefanie and Brent Ritchie
Tel: 03 7311008
SH 6, Punakaiki
Fax: 03 7311118
Email: PunakaikiMotel@minidata.co.nz

Double/twin: $80-110

Evening meals available at nearby tavern (400m).
Note: Postal address PO Box 54, Greymouth.

Greymouth
Golden Coast Bed & Breakfast
Glad Roche
Tel: 03 7687839
10 Smith Street, Greymouth
Fax: 03 7687869

Double/twin: $70-75

Maryglen Homestay
Glen and Allison Palmer
Tel: 03 7680706
20 Weenink Road, Karoro, Greymouth
Fax: 03 7680599
Mob: 025 380479
Email: maryglen@minidata.co.nz

Double/twin: $65-80

Welcome to beautiful bush setting overlooking the sea.

Oak Lodge
Zelda Anderson
Tel: 03 7686832
SH 6, Coal Creek
Greymouth
Fax: 03 7684362

Single: $90
Double/twin: $95-130
Breakfast: Cooked
Beds: 2D 2S
Evening meal: Not available
Bathrooms: 3EN

Situated 4km north of Greymouth. Rural surroundings. Built 1902. Décor antique furniture. Swimming pool and spa. Relaxing atmosphere.

The Breakers
Dot and Bill Dee
Tel: 03 7627743
Coast Road, Nine Mile Creek
Fax: 03 7627733
North Greymouth
Email: breakers@minidata.co.nz

Single: $85-100
Double: $95-145
Breakfast: Cooked
Beds: 1Q 2D
Evening meal: $27.50pp
Bathrooms: 3EN

Spectacular ocean views from 2 acres of grounds on the Coast Road 14 kms north of Greymouth, 35ks from the Pancake Rocks at Punakaiki.

Hokitika
Aroha Riverstay
Robert and Christine Warman
Tel: 03 7555082
102 Gibson Quay, Hokitika
Fax: 03 7556452

Double/twin: $70

Kingsize bed (1.8 m wide), separate entrance, separate shower/toilet.

McCarthy Homestay
Brian and Berna McCarthy **Double/twin:** $75
Tel: 03 7557599
70 Tudor Street, Hokitika
One Kilometre to glowworms, town centre, restaurants.

Franz Josef Glacier
Westwood Lodge

Bill and Janet Gawn
Tel: 03 7520111
SH 6, Franz Josef, Westland
Fax: 03 7520111
Free: 0800 741111
Email: westwood.lodge@minidata.co.nz

Single: $145
Double/twin: $145-175
Breakfast: Cooked
Beds: 4D 2S
Evening meal: Not available
Bathrooms: 6EN

The lodge, in a rural setting with mountain views, offers comfort and quiet with a lounge and a billiard room. Breakfast is either continental or cooked and tea, coffee and home baking are available 24 hours a day. All this within easy access to the wonders of the glacier country.

Bruce Bay
Mulvaney Farmstays
Peter and Malai Millar
Tel: 03 7510865
Condons Road, Bruce Bay
South Westland
Fax: 03 7510865

Single: $50
Double/twin: $75
Breakfast: Continental
Beds: 1D 2S
Evening meal: $20pp
Bathrooms: 1FS

We invite you to spend quality time with us on our farm in a World Heritage Park. Central for travellers, between Haast and Glaciers. Thai / European meals on request.

Haast
Okuru Beach Homestay Bed & Breakfast
Derek and Marian Beynon **Double/twin:** $60
Tel: 03 7500719
Jackson Bay Road,
Okuru, Haast
Fax: 03 7500722

Experience the scenic beauty of the west coast.

CANTERBURY/OTAGO PAGES 94 - 117

- Kaikoura
- Hanmer Springs
- Culverden
- Gore Bay
- Arthurs Pass
- Oxford
- Amberley/Waipara
- Christchurch
- Lake Coleridge
- Methven/Mt Mutt
- Akaroa
- Rakaia
- Ashburton
- Geraldine
- Timaru
- Oamaru
- Palmerston
- Lawrence
- Dunedin
- Waihola
- Gore
- Owaka
- Riverton
- Invercargill
- Stewart Island

Christchurch

Kaikoura
Dylans Country Stay

Mike and Maureen Morris
Tel: 03 3195473
Postmans Road
Kaikoura
Canterbury

Single: $80-95
Double/twin: $80-95
Breakfast: Continental
Beds: 1Q 1D 1S
Evening meal: Not available
Bathrooms: 2PR

Dylans offers two unique private rustic cottages finished in macrocapa which was felled and milled on the property.
Awaken to the sound of native birds, stroll through the totally organic vegetable and flower gardens and on your private patio enjoy a breakfast of homemade bread, jams and preserves. For privacy no better place could be found, but remember your friendly hosts are always willing to share their home and hospitality with you.

The Gums

Ian and Alison Boyd
Tel: 03 3195736
Schoolhouse Road, Kaikoura
Fax: 03 3195732
Free: 0800 226164
Email: The.gums@xtra.co.nz

Single: $50
Double/twin: $80-85
Breakfast: Continental
Beds: 3Q 1S
Evening meal: Not available
Bathrooms: 3EN

You will enjoy a relaxed and peaceful stay in a beautiful rural setting near the magnificent Kaikoura mountains. This land was bought by my great, great, uncle in 1883 and he milked cows here. You can relax in a choice of three ensuite bedrooms with queen size beds, TV, fridge, settee, coffee & tea facilities. You will have your own private entrance and you can come and go as you please. Off street parking, laundry facilities. Adjacent to our property is a dairy farm you can visit. You are 5 minutes from tourist attractions and restaurants. Tours arranged. Ian is a retired teacher and Alison is a Librarian. Hobbies include tennis, golf, designing and building houses, gardening, travel, handicrafts and spinning. You are welcome to try your hand at spinning. We look forward to your company. There is an Irish garden bar and restaurant within walking distance.
Directions: Driving north 4kms from Kaikoura on SH1, turn left, 1.5km along Schoolhouse road.

Clematis Grove

Ken and Margaret Hamilton
Tel: 03 3195264
Blue Duck Valley, Kaikoura
Fax: 03 3195278
Mob: 025 2421959

Single: $55
Double/twin: $75
Breakfast: Continental
Beds: 1D 2S
Evening meal: $25pp
Bathrooms: 1PR

Come and enjoy our modern fully self-contained two bedroomed flat. We are in a beautiful bushclad valley. Hear the birds. Also large lounge with pool table. Note: The two single beds can become one king.

Hilltop Bed and Breakfast

David and Kathy Mallinder
Tel: 03 3195624
74 Churchill Street, Kaikoura
Fax: 03 3195624
Email: davidmallinder@xtra.co.nz

Double/twin: $65

Sea and mountain views, pick up's, barbecue area.

Waitane Homestay

Kathleen and Peter King
Tel: 03 3195494
Waitane Road, Oaro, Kaikoura

Double/twin: $65

Rural setting, sea views, wonderful coastal walk.

Hanmer Springs
Northern Castle Guest House

Rose and Ernie Ball
Tel: 03 3157492
148 Hanmer Springs Road,
Hanmer Springs

Single: $45
Double/twin: $60
Breakfast: Continental
Beds: 1K 1Q 1D 2S
Evening meal: Not available
Bathrooms: 1GS

Rose and Ernie welcome you to their home set in 1/2 acre peaceful garden. 1 km from Hanmer Village. Downstairs exclusively for guests. Tea making facilities, continental breakfast served upstairs, cooked breakfast on request. Handy to golf links, horse trecking, hot pools, bungy jumping, jet boating, helicopter rides and beautiful mountain views.

Champagne Flat

Chris and Virginia Parsons
Tel: 03 3157413
Hanmer Springs
Fax: 03 3157412

Double/twin: $90

Warm, comfortable country house with a million dollar view!

Shining Cuckoo Guest House

Val Mooney
Tel: 03 3157095
Cheltenham Street, Hanmer Springs

Double/twin: $50

Culverden
Pahau Pastures Bed & Breakfast

Diana Bethell
Tel: 03 3158023
Pahau Pastures, Culverden
North Canterbury
Fax: 03 3158023
Mob: 025 362530

Single: $55
Double/twin: $110
Breakfast: Cooked
Beds: 1D 4S
Evening meal: $35pp
Bathrooms: 1EN 2PR

Pahau Pastures has been in the Bethell family for 120 years and is situated 100ks from Christchurch and 4.5ks off Highway 7. We have 3,500 acres of sheep and beef farming and border dyke irrigation. Our homestead is a large kauri historic home, situated in parklike surroundings of mature trees and a large garden currently being restored, with a rose walk, drystone wall, and a feature of daffodills in Spring, and beautiful views which were all featured in N.Z House and Garden and on TV. Dinner is by arrangement, served in the formal dining room, and picnic lunches are available. Local activities include hot thermal pools, bungy jumping, jet boating, bushwalks,ski-ing, fishing, golf, Maori rock art, local wineries and 1 1/2 hours to Kaikoura whale watch. We assure you of a warm welcome and invite you to relax in our tranquil home and garden or around our roaring open fire.

Gore Bay
Caesar Courts
Peter and Valerie McClatchy
Tel: 03 3198535
6 Cathedral Road, Gore Bay
North Canterbury

Double/twin: $55-60

Beachfront, great views, bush walks, swimming, friendly hosts.

Amberley/Waipara
Bredon Downs Homestay

Bob and Veronica Lucy
Tel: 03 3149356
Amberley
North Canterbury
Fax: 03 3148994
Mob: 025 2244061

Single: $50
Double/twin: $90
Breakfast: Cooked
Beds: 1Q 3S
Evening meal: $25pp
Bathrooms: 1GS

We are just south of Amberley and 40 minutes north of Christchurch, within easy reach of the airport and conveniently on the road to and from the Picton ferry. Our farmhouse is surrounded by an English-style garden and only a few minutes drive from the Waipara wineries. We breed ostriches and are only too pleased to show these to visitors.

The Good Life
June and Lennie Harrison
Tel: 03 3143720
549 Scargill Valley Road, Greta Valley
Fax: 03 3143447

Double/twin: $100

Organic farm, organic food, house cow. Dinner available.

Arthurs Pass
Chalet B & B
Michael Bohny
Tel: 03 3189236
SH 73, Arthurs Pass Village
Fax: 03 3189200
Free: 0800 506550

Single: $95
Double/twin: $105
Breakfast: Continental
Beds: 8D
Evening meal: $22pp
Bathrooms: 8EN 2GS

Beautifully appointed individually decorated rooms. Our speciality is fine dining using the best of local ingredients including venison, lamb and salmon. Come experience the difference!

Oxford
Country Life B&B
Norton and Helen Dunn
Tel: 03 3124167
137 High Street, Oxford

Double/twin: $60-70

Twin room $60, self-contained unit with cooking facilities $70.

Twin Bridge Farm Stays B&B
Don and Anne Manera
Tel: 03 3124964
345 Woodside Road, Coopers Creek
Oxford

Double/twin: $70

Dinner available. Lovely views, tramping, fishing, jet boating.

Lake Coleridge
Lake Coleridge Lodge

Mark and Trish Barr
Tel: 03 3185002
Lake Coleridge
Canterbury
Fax: 03 3185002

Single: $60
Double/twin: $80
Breakfast: Cooked
Beds: 3D 8S
Evening meal: $20pp
Bathrooms: 3GS

Mark and Trish welcome you to their peaceful haven. Off the usual tourist track, away from the bustle of city life you can enjoy fabulous fishing, bush walking, our unique winter golf course, nearby ski fields, and enjoy majestic scenery. We have facilities for the disabled, and welcome pet dogs. (Kennels available)

Christchurch
Cashmere Heights B&B

Karen and Barry Newman
Tel: 03 3321778
6 Allom Lane, Christchurch
Fax: 03 3329399
Mob: 025 2410911
Email: rover@iconz.co.nz

Single: $90
Double/twin: $150-165
Breakfast: Special
Beds: 3K
Evening meal: $30pp
Bathrooms: 1GS

We invite you to spend some time in our near new home, nestled high on the Port Hills Christchurch. Cashmere Heights captures the "million dollar" views with 180 degree panorama from the ocean, across the city and Canterbury Plains, to the Southern Alps. We are only a ten minute drive to the city centre and 400 metres to the historic sign of the Takahe restaurant. Our guest accommodation is located on a separate level of our home, ensuring privacy and relaxation. All rooms are large and individually decorated in bold colours, enhancing our desire to create and maintain a relaxing holiday and homely environment. The guest lounge is large and offers tea/coffee facilities, home theatre, reading area, computer station, phone/fax. Adjoining the lounge is a sun deck with outdoor furniture, BBQ and spa pool. We also provide courtesy guest pick up and a luxury tour service with Rover Tours. Note: Not suitable for children.
Internet: www.nz-holiday.co.nz/cashmere

Eliza's Manor House

Lynn and Michael Smith
Tel: 03 3668584
82 Bealey Avenue, Christchurch
Fax: 03 3664946
Free: 03 3661073
Email: elizas@ihug.co.nz

Single: $70
Double/twin: $95
Breakfast: Continental
Beds: 4K 3Q 3D 3S
Evening meal: Not available
Bathrooms: 8EN 1GS 1FS

Eliza's is a superb gracious Victorian mansion, built in 1860, and lovingly restored.
The original architectural gems including a magnificent entrance foyer, coloured lead light windows and banquet room are complimented with comfortable beds and most with their own en-suite. The tariff includes continental buffet breakfast. Eliza's is a very comfortable and restful place to stay where you can relax and enjoy the convivial atmosphere. We are a short pleasant drive from the airport and conveniently situated 10-15 minutes level walk to Art centre, Botanical gardens, Art galleries, City centre, golf course, museums, restaurants. Eliza's is set well back from the street with magnificent trees, courtyard gardens and off street parking.
We offer complimentary tea, coffee, hot chocolate anytime, a cosy lounge to meet new friends, and an olde-English style bar.
We look forward to sharing the delights of Eliza's with you.
Please fax, ring or write your bookings to us.
We extend a warm welcome to you.

Fairleigh Garden Guest House

Allan and Valerie Carleton
Tel: 03 3593538
411 Sawyers Arms Road, Harewood
Christchurch
Fax: 03 3593548
Mob: 025 2243746
Free: 0800 611411

Single: $80
Double/twin: $135
Breakfast: Special
Beds: 2Q 2S
Evening meal: $25pp
Bathrooms: 2EN 1PR

Your hosts Allan and Valerie welcome you to Christchurch's best kept secret - only 4 minutes from the airport. Our country style cedarwood house has NZ heart rimu throughout with quality furnishings and native timber antique dressers. Each well dressed bedroom has luxury bedding, fresh flowers, TV, telephone, hair dryer, electric blanket, modern ensuites - all the comforts of home. Delectable breakfasts or fresh fruits, juice, yoghurt, cereal, homemade bread, preserves and specially cooked breakfast options. Splendid lunches, delicious dinners and NZ BBQs are available by arrangement. The large tranquil cottage garden has many interesting areas to explore - the lily pond, gazebo, rose covered arches, many deciduous trees, herbs and vegetables. Enjoy croquet and petanque on the lawn surrounded by perennials. Explore the local countryside on our bicycles. Come and enjoy NZ hospitality at its best! Quote: "Beautiful peaceful gardens, warm comfortable rooms, delightful home cooked breakfasts and friendly hosts - its all so wonderful" Cheng Siew Lin, Kuala Lumpur, Malaysia.

Windsor Private Hotel

Carol Healey   Don Evans
Tel: 03 3661503
52 Armagh Street, Christchurch
Fax: 03 3669796

Single: $60
Double/twin: $90
Breakfast: Cooked
Beds: 18D 8S
Evening meal: Not available
Bathrooms: 24GS

The Windsor, originally named Warwick House, was built at the turn of the century. Set in the quiet north-west situation of Cranmer Square - centrally located on the Tourist Tram route, the hotel is within 5 to 10 minutes walk of the city centre, restaurants, Town Hall, Casino, Art Centre, Museum and Botanical Gardens. Guests are greeted on arrival and shown around our charming colonial style home, often described as "traditional". Our nicely furnished bedrooms are all individually heated, with the shared bathroom facilities, conveniently appointed for guests comfort, bathrobes on request. Our generous morning break-fast menu includes fruit juice, fresh fruits, and cereal followed by bacon and eggs, sasuages, tomatoes, toast and marmalade and served in the dining room (between 6.30 and 9.00 am). The lounge, where we offer tea, coffee and biscuits each evening at 9 pm is where everyone gathers to watch TV and have a chat. There are 24 hour tea, coffee, and laundry facilities along with off street parking for the motorist. With consideration for our guests, we encourage non-smoking. Please note triple and quad rooms are available. Quote this book for 10% discount.

Hadleigh Homestay

David and Betty Purdue
Tel: 03 3557174
6 Eversleigh Street
Christchurch
Fax: 03 3557174

Single: $140
Double/twin: $160
Breakfast: Cooked
Beds: 2Q
Evening meal: Not available
Bathrooms: 2EN

We welcome you to enjoy Hadleigh, our elegant listed historic home in a romantic garden. Easy walk to Cathedral Square. Guest lounge, billiard room, antiques and art. Each room has electric blankets and heaters, tea and coffee facilities and TV. No smoking.
Allergy sufferers please note we have family pets.

Christchurch Pier B&B
Joyce Lavender
Tel: 03 3882190
533 Pages Road, New Brighton
Christchurch
Fax: 03 3880431

Single: $56
Double/twin: $80-99
Breakfast: Special
Beds: 1K 1Q 1D 6S
Evening meal: Not available
Bathrooms: 3EN 1GS

Your hosts Joyce and Des would love to welcome you to our sunny spacious homestay. We are situated in the seaside suburb of New Brighton within easy walking distance of New Zealand's only pier.

Hamilton House Bed & Breakfast
Glen and Jill Travis
Tel: 03 3295188
Curries Road, Springston , Christchurch
Fax: 03 3295189
Mob: 025 2263589
Email: hamilton.house@xtra.co.nz

Double/twin: $100-120

Historic character villa, elegant ensuite rooms, tranquil gardens.

Highcroft Country Club
Robin and Eliza Quinn
Tel: 03 3296658
Old Tai Tapu Road
Christchurch
Fax: 03 3296827

Single: $180
Double/twin: $200
Breakfast: Extra charge
Beds: 1K 4Q 1D 10S
Evening meal: $45pp
Bathrooms: 6EN

Modern colonial style homestead in 10 acres of formal gardens and farmland. 20 minutes from airport and central city. Restaurant, billiards, swimming, spa, sauna, tennis. Continental breakfast $11pp, special $18.50pp.

Kleynbos Homestay B&B
Gerda de Kleyne   Hans van den Bos   **Double/twin:** $65-85
Tel: 03 3322896
59 Ngaio Street, St Martins, Christchurch
Fax: 03 3322896
Mob: 025 2234144
Email: Lucien.Dol@xtra.co.nz

Large ensuite bedrooms, self-catering optional charming house, excellent value for money.

Locarno Self Catering Apartment
Aileen and David Davies   **Double/twin:** $80-100
Tel: 03 3329987
25 Locarno Street, Opawa, Christchurch
Fax: 03 3329687
Mob: 025 399747

Self contained luxury peaceful garden apartment, close city.

Treeview
Kathy and Laurence Carr   **Double/twin:** $60
Tel: 03 3842352
6 Lomond Place,
Woolston - Linwood, Christchurch

Akaroa
Lavaud House

Francis and Frances Gallagher
Tel: 03 3047121
83 Rue Lavaud, Akaroa
Banks Peninsula
Fax: 03 3047121

Single: $60
Double/twin: $80-100
Breakfast: Continental
Beds: 1K 2Q 2S
Evening meal: Not available
Bathrooms: 2EN 1GS

Francis and Frances extend you a warm welcome to Lavaud House, our lovely old, well-restored, early Edwardian residence, over-looking the main Akaroa beach and harbour. Within 2 minutes walk of shops and restaurants, we enjoy a large tranquil garden, with native birds, and panoramic harbour views. All bedrooms are very comfortable with heaters, television and electric blankets.

The large guest sitting room is warm and sunny with a glorious harbour view, books, piano, television and tea or coffee on request.

Joy's Bed & Breakfast

Joy Luisetti
Tel: 03 3047137
Bella-Vista, 21B Watson Street, Akaroa
Fax: 03 3047137
Mob: 025 779168

Double/twin: $75-95

Peaceful, spectacular views, bush and harbour walks, exotic cuisine.

Kawatea Farmstay

Judy and Kerry Thacker
Tel: 03 3048621
Okains Bay
Banks Peninsula
Fax: 03 3048621

Single: $55
Double/twin: $90-100
Breakfast: Special
Beds: 2Q 1D 2S
Evening meal: $25pp
Bathrooms: 1EN 1GS

24 hour hospitality in historic homestead in one of the beautiful bays of Banks Peninsula. Coastal walks with panoramic views from the 540 hectare farm.

Otanga Matua

Gwen and Murray Manhire
Tel: 03 3045055
Barrys Bay, Banks Peninsula

Double/twin: $80

Be at home and welcome in our home.

Rakaia
St Ita's Guesthouse

Ken and Miriam Cutforth
Tel: 03 3027546
Barrhill/Methven Road, Rakaia
Canterbury
Fax: 03 3027546

Single: $60
Double/twin: $90
Breakfast: Cooked
Beds: 3D 2S
Evening meal: $25pp
Bathrooms: 3EN

Welcome to St Ita's, our spacious former Convent (1912). Large, comfortable guestrooms have modern ensuites; an open fire warms the wood-panelled lounge. We serve generous 'home-grown' meals. St Ita's is located on the western edge of Rakaia Township. Rakaia has great salmon fishing and is close to Mt Hutt and Christchurch.

Methven/Mt Hutt
Mt Hutt Station Homestead

Brian and Karen Schultze
Tel: 03 3028130
Rakaia Gorge, Mt Hutt
Canterbury
Fax: 03 3028102

Single: $90
Double/twin: $125
Breakfast: Cooked
Beds: 6D 12S
Evening meal: Restaurant
Bathrooms: 9EN

Beautifully situated on a privately owned 8000 acre deer station equipped with every conceivable facility from a top class restaurant to a scenic jet boat ride. A place to experience the magic of the New Zealand way of life - at first hand and at its best. We invite you to enjoy abundant natural beauty - and indulge yourself in the genuine, relaxed style of the South Island hospitality. For those with the total holiday in mind, from the subdued to the adventurous, we can cater to your every need. Hunting and fishing safaris by arrangement depending on the time of year. Short bush walks around the Homestead with trees well over 100 years old, try feeding the trout in our large tank with viewing glass. Relaxation at the end of your day - Spa, House Bar, Games Room, Souvenir Shop, Guest Lounge with roaring open log fire.

Chelsea Lodge
Elaine Smith   **Double/twin:** $85
Tel: 03 3182700
Charles Street, Glentunnel, Canterbury
Fax: 03 3182700

Scenic Route. English style. Skiing, golf, fishing, TranzAlpine

Pagey's Farmstay
Shirley and Gene Pagey   **Double/twin:** $80
Tel: 03 3021713
Methven Chertsey Road, Methven,
Mt Hutt, Canterbury
Fax: 03 3021714
Mob: 025 365513

Ashburton
Carradale Farm
Jim and Karen McIntyre   **Double/twin:** $80
Tel: 03 3086577
200 Ferriman's Road, Lagmhor,
Ashburton
Fax: 03 3086548
Mob: 025 338044

Weatherly House
Helen Thomson   **Double/twin:** $65
Tel: 03 3089949
359 West Street, Ashburton

Weir Homestay
Pat and Dave Weir   **Double/twin:** $60
Tel: 03 3083534
1 Sudbury Street
Ashburton

'Rather see the wonders of the world abroad than, living dully sluggardized at home, wear out thy youth with shapeless idleness.' - **Shakespeare**

Geraldine
The Gardeners Cottage

Carolyn Hay   Eddie Cook
Tel: 03 6938205
85 Pye Rd, The Downs,
Geraldine
Fax: 03 6938205

Single: $105
Double/twin: $125
Breakfast: Continental
Beds: 1Q 1S
Evening meal: $35pp
Bathrooms: 1EN

Eddie and Carolyn invite you to come and relax in the peace and quiet of our country environment. Our self-contained cottage offers your own privacy. We have a swimming pool available for your use. There are many artists and potters in our region and Eddie has a studio on the property for sculpture. Geraldine has two fine golf courses and plenty of bush walks. Jet boating, fishing, skiing, scenic flights, rafting are all easily accessible; or go tramping and explore Mt Peel or other mountains in our region. Alternatively, just relax in the cottage and enjoy the mountain scenery. We are the ideal stop-over between Christchurch and Mt. Cook/Queenstown and beyond.
We look forward to welcoming you to our area.

Camelot Gardens Homestay

Barry and Daphne
Tel: 03 6938559
Ribbonwood Road, The Downs, Geraldine

Double/twin: $45-80

Congenial, quiet Kiwi style accommodation in beautiful surroundings.

Hislop House

Jan Hey
Tel: 03 6938890
20 Cox Street, Geraldine
Fax: 03 6938890

Double/twin: $70

A warm friendly WELCOME awaits you. Complimentary tea/coffee.

Timaru
Jan's Place

Jan Baker
Tel: 03 6884589
4A Rose Street, Timaru

Double/twin: $55

Central character villa, homely, courtesy services, best value.

Oamaru
Blue Penguin Lodge

Elizabeth and Evan Niven
Tel: 03 4347027
2 Chelmer Street
Oamaru
Fax: 03 4347027

Single: $70
Double/twin: $70
Breakfast: Cooked
Beds: 1Q 4S
Evening meal: $25pp
Bathrooms: 1PR 1GS

Our charming 1910 "Gentlemans Residence" stands on 1/4 acre of mature trees and garden and features kauri timber, ornate fire surrounds and pressed metal ceilings. There are 3 guest bedrooms, 1 queen, 2 twin, each with its own individual charm and a comfortable lounge with television, tea and coffee facilities.

We are situated only one block from SH 1 at the southern end of Oamaru behind the public gardens and close to all shopping and amenities, Blue Penguin and Yellow-eyed Penguin colonies, Forrester Gallery, Museum and historic port. Excellent golf courses, salmon, trout and sea fishing are all closeby plus many other attractions for the discerning traveller to find. Elizabeth has a background in travel and tourism and interests in music, floral art and photography. Evan has also been involved in travel and has a baking background. He is also a keen golfer, fisherman and photographer. We look forward to welcoming you to our home and the many interesting attractions Oamaru is waiting to unfold for your enjoyment.

Innwoodleigh Homestay

Howard and Vennessa
Tel: 03 4370829
39 Forth Street
Oamaru
Fax: 03 4370829

Single: $55
Double/twin: $110-150
Breakfast: Continental
Beds: 1D 2S
Evening meal: Not available
Bathrooms: 1PR

Our home allows our guests a peaceful 'time out' on your own exclusive level of the house. Aromatherapy oils for your spa bath and the opportunity to go deep sea fishing on our boat the Dolphin. Honeymooners package ($150 per night) includes: Flowers - your colour choice - keep, bottle of wine, massage oil, cooked breakfast.

Anne Mieke Guest House
Sally and Des Cochrane   Double/twin: $60
Tel: 03 4348051
47 Tees Street, Oamaru
Fax: 03 4348050
Email: anne.mieke@xtra.co.nz

Quiet location, harbour views, close to Penguin colony.

Clyde House Homestay
Wenda and John Eason   Double/twin: $80
Tel: 03 4372774
32 Clyde Street, Oamaru
Fax: 03 4372774

Spacous garden setting, return veranda, oamaru stone built1909.

Cumbria
Pamela and Wilson Spite   Double/twin: $85
Tel: 03 4345276
Oamaru
Fax: 03 4345276

Historic home 3kms penguins. Large garden. Haute cuisine.

Earth Brick House
Michael O'Brien   Kahren Thompson   Double/twin: $70
Tel: 03 4346210
8 Matfen Street, Oamaru

Sea views, coastal walks, rare penguins, near town.

Glen Haven Bed & Breakfast

Betty and Brian Lloyd
Tel: 03 4370211
5 Forth Street, Oamaru
Fax: 03 4370211

Double/twin: $60

Budget rates - Quality accommodation. 1 separate unit - 1 triple room in house.

Springbank Garden Flat

Joan and Stan Taylor
Tel: 03 4346602
60 Weston Road, Oamaru
Fax: 03 4346602

Double/twin: $50

New self-contained flat in attractive garden.
Double bed and bed settee.

Palmerston
Shag Valley Station

Louise and Alf Bell
Tel: 03 4650821
Palmerston
Otago
Fax: 03 4650821

Single: $80
Double/twin: $140
Breakfast: Cooked
Beds: 4S
Evening meal: $30pp
Bathrooms: 1EN 1PR

Sheep and cattle station. Extensive garden, historic scientific and radio museum. Shag Valley is 25km from Palmerston on Highway 85 when driving towards Queenstown.

Kaikoura

Dunedin
Sahara Guest House

Lynette Ryder
Tel: 03 4776662
619 George Street, Dunedin
Fax: 03 4792551

Single: $53-63
Double/twin: $80-84
Breakfast: Cooked
Beds: 1K 2Q 2D 10S
Evening meal: Not available
Bathrooms: 2EN 3GS

This gabled brick guesthouse was built as a substantial family home in 1906.It now holds 10 rooms: 2 with ensuites; 8 (with handbasins in each room) share the 2 bathrooms which have a total of 5 separate showers, 1 bath and three toilets.

The house is centrally located; just a short walk to city centre, botanic gardens, museum, Otago University and is on a major bus route. The hearty breakfast served in our bright dining room consists of a buffet style continental as well as a cooked breakfast menu. Evening dining can be enjoyed at any of the local hotels, cafes or restaurants which are within easy walking distance.

The house is kept warm and cosy with central heating as well as additional heaters in the bedrooms and electric blankets on all beds. Laundry facilities are available for our guests and off street parking for those who require it. The "Sahara" also has fully self contained units available for those travellers wanting accommodation with private facilities, kitchen, television and telephones in each unit.

Gowrie House

Vivienne and Rod Nye
Tel: 03 4772103
7 Gowry Place, Roslyn
Dunedin
Fax: 03 4772103

Single: $50
Double/twin: $80
Breakfast: Continental
Beds: 1D 2S
Evening meal: Not available
Bathrooms: 1GS 1FS

For fun and laughter, warm and sunny rooms, and good company in comfortable surroundings, stay with Rod and Vivienne at Gowrie House. We are 5 minutes drive from the centre of the city - 20 on foot. We will happily give you information about all of Dunedin's easily-accessible and superb attractions.

Averleigh Cottage
Joanne McKellar
Tel: 03 4558829
St Clair, Dunedin
Fax: 03 4556380
Mob: 021 631725
Email: joanne@averleigh.co.nz

Double/twin: $185

View our web site: www.averleigh.co.nz

Deacons Court Bed and Breakfast
Karen and Dene Mackenzie
Tel: 03 4779053
342 High Street, Dunedin
Fax: 03 4779058
Email: deacons@es.co.nz

Single: $70
Double/twin: $110-120
Breakfast: Cooked
Beds: 3D 3S
Evening meal: Not available
Bathrooms: 2EN 1PR

Deacons court is an historic home a short walk from the centre of Dunedin. Our generous breakfasts include the choice of continental, with either hot muffins or homemade bread, or full cooked.

Harbour Lookout
Ron and Maire Graham
Tel: 03 4710582
3 Taupo Street, Ravensbourne, Dunedin

Double/twin: $60

A warm welcome awaits in a comfortable home.

Nisbet Cottage
Hildegard Lubake
Tel: 03 4545169
6A Elliffe Place, Shiel Hill, Dunedin
Fax: 03 4545369
Email: wingsok@ex.co.nz

Double/twin: $95-110

Homestay hospitality with hotel comforts. Peaceful and quiet.

The Mission
Pat and Phillipa Cummings Double/twin: $85+
Tel: 03 4761321
Mission Cove, Company Bay, Otago Peninsula
Fax: 03 4761028
Mob: 025 751782
Email: cummings@deepsouth.co.nz

Refurbished ex-nurses home in tranquil surroundings, spacious and comfortable.

Waihola
'Ivy Cottage' Lakeside Homestay
Bryan and Robin Leckie Double/twin: $65
Tel: 03 4178946
7 SH 1, Waihola, Otago
Fax: 03 4178966

Lawrence
The Ark

Frieda Betman
Tel: 03 4859328
8 Harrington Place
Lawrence

Single: $33
Double/twin: $60-70
Breakfast: Special
Beds: 2D 1S
Evening meal: $15pp
Bathrooms: 1FS

On main road Dunedin end, through poplar avenue by "welcome to Lawrence" sign. The ark lovingly restored is set in half acre flower garden. Cuppa awaits you on arrival. Frieda will show you highlights of the old goldmining town or you may wish to explore for yourself. Happy relaxed atmosphere. Note: One childs bed also available.

Fairview Farmstay
Rob and Kaye French Double/twin: $75
Tel: 03 4859855
Waitahuna, Otago
Fax: 03 4859855

Comfortable historic homestead just 1km from SH 8.

Owaka
Kepplestone Park Homestay
Gay and Arch Maley
Tel: 03 4158134
Surat Bay Road, Newhaven, Owaka
Fax: 03 4158137
Free: 0800 105134

Single: $60
Double/twin: $60-85
Breakfast: Special
Beds: 2D 2S
Evening meal: $25pp
Bathrooms: 2EN

We invite you to share our wonderful location. Close to beach with Hooker seals and near penguins and Purakaunui falls. Separate guest unit with ensuites.

Tarara Downs Farmstay
Ida and John Burgess   **Double/twin:** $55
Tel: 03 4158293
Owaka, South Otago

Nearest house to the Purakauni Falls. Dinner $15pp.

Gore
Kowhai Place Farmstay
John and Helen   **Double/twin:** $70
Tel: 03 2038774
291 Glendhu Road, Mataura, Gore
Fax: 03 2038774

Dinner available. Lovely views, good fishing rivers and golf course.

Invercargill
Catlins Farmstay
June and Murray Stratford   **Double/twin:** $80-90
Tel: 03 2468843
174 Progress Valley Road, RD 1, Tokanui
Fax: 03 2468844

1000 acre farm tour. Great scenery and food

The Grove Deer Farm
Alex and Eileen Henderson   **Single:** $40
Tel: 03 2166492   **Double/twin:** $60
154 Oteramika Road, Invercargill
Fax: 03 2166492

Tudor Park
Joyce and John Robins   **Double/twin:** $70
Tel: 03 2217150
21 Lawrence Road, Ryal Bush, Invercargill
Fax: 03 2217150
Mob: 025 310031

A warm welcome, comfort, privacy, tranquility and country food.

Riverton
Riverton Rock
Jane and Evan Bloomfield   **Double/twin:** $78
Tel: 03 2348886
136 Palmerston Street, Riverton
Fax: 03 2348816   Mob: 025 359591
Free: 0800 248886   Email: therock@riverton.co.nz

Gracefully restored historic hotel in sleepy fishing village.

Stewart Island
Thorfinn Charters
Bruce Story   BJ McKay   **Single** $50
Tel: 03 2191210   **Double/twin:** $90
Halfmoon Bay, Stewart Island   **Breakfast:** Continental
Fax: 03 2191210   **Beds:** 6D 6S
Email: thorfinn@southnet.co.nz   **Evening meal:** $25pp
       Bathrooms: 1EN 2PR

B&B Homestay with ensuite. Also 2 self-contained houses, sleep 7. Linen, central heating, transfers. Superb views, beach, qualmark(applied for), launch charter, bird/wildlife viewing/photography, nature walks. $15 per extra person in S/C. Breakfast materials available S/C also.

Queenstown

Omarama
Glenburn Park Homestay

Alan and Marie Campbell　　　　**Double/twin:** $70
Tel: 03 4389624
SH 83, Lake Benmore, Omarama
Fax: 03 4389624
Email: glenburn.park@xtra.co.nz

Lakeside accommodation. Sleepmaker mattresses.
Great fishing (resident guide.)

The Briars

Marylou and Don Blue　　　　**Double/twin:** $70
Tel: 03 4389615
Ahuriri Heights, SH 8, Omarama
Fax: 03 4389655

Homestay near Mt Cook. Charming antique furnished home.

Wanaka
Oak Ridge Lodge

Robyn Lindsay　　　　**Single:** $95
Tel: 03 4437707　　　　**Double/twin:** $110
Cnr Cardrona and Orchard Road　　**Breakfast:** Continental
Wanaka　　　　**Beds:** 4K
Central Otago　　　　**Evening meal:** Not available
Fax: 03 4437750　　　　**Bathrooms:** 4EN
Email: lodge@voyager.co.nz

Surrounded by the majestic snow-capped mountains of Aspiring National Park and the picturesque Cardrona Valley, this purpose-built lodge set in 25 acres of tree-studded lawns, gardens and pasture includes a spacious, comfortable lounge with pool table, piano, very large screen T.V. and log fire, and 4 comfortable king bedrooms, all with ensuites.

Te Wanaka Lodge

Rowland and Nora Hastings
Tel: 03 4439224
23 Brownston Street, Wanaka,
Central Otago
Fax: 03 4439246
Free: 0508 926252
Email: tewanakalodge@xtra.co.nz

Single: $100-125
Double/twin: $110-115
Breakfast: Special
Beds: 8Q 8S
Evening meal: Not available
Bathrooms: 12EN

Nestled in the heart of Wanaka against a backdrop of alpine grandeur, Te Wanaka Lodge offers architecturally designed contemporary accommodation. It is located within east walking distance of shops, restaurants, the lakeshore and golf course. Spacious breakfast room, 2 comfortable guest lounges with log fire, garden hot tub, international art collection.

Aspiring Images
Betty and George Russell
Tel: 03 4438358
26 Norman Terrace, Wanaka, Central Otago
Fax: 03 4438327
Email: grussell@xtra.co.nz

Double/twin: $80

'Handsome home;' 'Beautiful location;' 'Caring hosts;' 'Great value!'

Glens of Roy
Trevor and Kate Norman
Tel: 03 4437392
Mt Aspiring Road, Wanaka
Fax: 03 4437848

Double/twin: $95

Spectacular lake and mountain views. Quality accommodation. 4km from township.

Hunt's Homestays
Bill and Ruth Hunt
Tel: 03 4431053
56 Manuka Crescent, Wanaka
Central Otago
Fax: 03 4431355

Single: $50
Double/twin: $80
Breakfast: Continental
Beds: 1D 2S
Evening meal: Not available
Bathrooms: 1GS

We would enjoy seeing you in our new home overlooking Lake Wanaka. The spacious ground floor rooms have spectacular views of lake and mountains.

Lake Hawea Fishing & Farmstay

Harris Urquhart **Double/twin:** $75
Tel: 03 4431535
33 Nook Road, Lake Hawea, Central Otago
Fax: 03 4431325

Self-contained farmstay accommodation and guided fishing trips.

Lake Wanaka Home Hosting

Joyce and Lex Turnbull **Double/twin:** $80-100
Tel: 03 4439060
19 Bills Way, Wanaka, Central Otago
Fax: 03 4431626
Mob: 025 2289160

With lake and mountain views. We enjoy your company.

River Run Lodge

Meg Taylor   John Pawson **Double/twin:** $240-260
Tel: 03 4439049
Halliday Road, SH 6, Wanaka, Central Otago
Fax: 03 4438454
Email: riverrun@xtra.co.nz

Luxury lodge on 420 riverside acres near Wanaka.

Temasek House

David and Poh Choo Turner
Tel: 03 4431288
7 Huchan Lane, Wanaka,
Central Otago
Fax: 03 4431288
Mob: 025 2779594

Single: $55
Double/twin: $80-90
Breakfast: Continental
Beds: 1Q 1D 1S
Evening meal: Not available
Bathrooms: 1PR 1GS

Superb location offering views of mountains and lake. Facilities include private guest area with extensive literature collection, laundry facilities, heating in all rooms and ample parking.
Children welcome.

The Apartment

Marjorie Goodger   Sheila McCaughan
Tel: 03 4437056
37 Noema Terrace, Lake Hawea
Central Otago
Fax: 03 4431807
Mob: 025 781911
Email: marge@xtra.co.nz

Single: $85
Double/twin: $85
Breakfast: Continental
Beds: 1D 1S
Evening meal: $25pp
Bathrooms: 1EN

Superior, affordable, new stand-alone apartment, mountain and lake views. Modern appliances including washing machine, dryer, dishwasher, video and stereo. Privacy and security assured. Private telephone.

Tirohanga Homestay

Ken and Noeleen McDiarmid **Double/twin:** $90
Tel: 03 4438302
102 Lismore Street, Wanaka, Central Otago
Fax: 03 4438302

Best grandstand view. Ample parking. 2 minutes from everything.

Arrowtown
Balfour B&B

Cynthia Balfour
Tel: 03 4421326
20 Wiltshire Street, Arrowtown
Central Otago

Beds: 1D 2S
Evening meal: Not available
Bathrooms: 1GS

A gardiners' delight in the heart of historic Arrowtown where you will find many unusual plants, as well as old favorites in an attractive cottage garden setting. Here a warm welcome awaits you in my homely, comfortable cottage. No effort is spared to make your stay interesting and memorable.

Perry Homestay
Claire and Alan Perry
Tel: 03 4425339
Coal Pit Road, Gibbston
Arrowtown
Fax: 03 4425339

Double/twin: $85

Stone cottage amongst vineyards. Lovely scenic walks - relaxing.

Queenstown
Bush Creek Health Retreat
Ileen Mutch
Tel: 03 4427260
21 Bowen Street
Queenstown
Fax: 03 4427250

Single: $50
Double/twin: $100
Breakfast: Special
Beds: 1Q 4S
Evening meal: not available
Bathrooms: 2GS

Re-energize. Renowned magical old world garden. Organically grown foods. All the extra home comforts. Within walking distance to the exalting throb Queenstown's activity is famed for.

Queenstown
Larch Hill

Elaine and Richard Bryant
Tel: 03 4424811
16 Panners Way, Goldfields
Queenstown
Fax: 03 4427128
Email: walk@inq.co.nz

Single: $75
Double/twin: $100-130
Breakfast: Special
Beds: 2K 4S
Evening meal: $35pp
Bathrooms: 2PR 1GS

All rooms overlook the shimmering clear blue waters of Lake Wakatipu, encircled by spectacular snow-capped mountains. This unique home provides a feeling of warmth and relaxation. A restful green theme spills through the bedrooms into the dining room and sitting room with its library, both opening to a sunny courtyard surrounded by cottage gardens. On arrival you will be greeted with fresh coffee and homemade muffins! Once you have settled in, relax in the courtyard garden, or take in the lake and mountain views from the sundeck. In winter there is a warm log fire awaiting your return from a days skiing or sightseeing tour. Your gourmet breakfast will set you up for the day to explore Queenstown's best kept secrets that we are happy to arrange for you. We are only three minutes by car to the centre of town, and public transport passes the driveway.
We welcome you to join us for a three course dinner, by prior arrangement. Note: Self contained appartment available.

DIRECTIONS: 3 km from Queenstown on Highway 6A from Frankton turn off 6A at Goldfields (Sherwood Manor). Second turn to left is Panners Way.

Ferry Hotel Guest House

Kevin and Glenys Reynolds
Tel: 03 4422194
Spence Road, Lower Shotover
Queenstown
Fax: 03 4422190
Email: ferry@clear.co.nz

Single: $100
Double/twin: $110-135
Breakfast: Special
Beds: 2D 2S
Evening meal: Not available
Bathrooms: 1EN 1GS

Old world elegance aptly describes this delightful historic guesthouse which is set in charming cottage gardens. Formerly a Hotel for over one hundred years and now lffering relaxing, cosy accommodation to modern day travellers. Historic photos line the walls and a roaring log fire in the lounge welcomes you. Use of the kitchen, which granny would have been proud of and laundry facilities are also available to guests.

The Dairy Guesthouse

Brian and Sarah Holding
Tel: 03 4425164
10 Isle Street, Queenstown
Fax: 03 4425164
Free: 0800 333393
Email: Thedairy@xtra.co.nz

Single: $125-140
Double/twin: $140-180
Breakfast: Cooked
Beds: 2K 4Q 2S
Evening meal: Enquire
Bathrooms: 7EN

Brian and Sarah Holding look forward to welcoming you to The Dairy Guethouse. The Dairy Guesthouse is just 150 metres from the town centre. The ideal central location from which to explore wonderful Queenstown and it's wide range of cultural, artistic and sporting activities. This very special place has a warm and cosy atmosphere, six private rooms (all with ensuite), lounge room with a wood fire, ski storage and parking. The Dairy, once a 1920's general store (a small piece of Queenstown history), now lovingly restored, where a full breakfast served every morning ensures a great start to the day. Surrounded by mountain views of the stunning Remarkables range, Coronet Peak and Lake Wakatipu. Conveniently situated below the Skyline Gondola on the corner of Brecon and Isle Streets. Note: The king beds can each convert to two singles.

BJ's Place
Berit Brown **Double/twin:** $100
Tel: 03 4428348
36 Lochy Road, Fernhill, Queenstown
Fax: 03 4428348

Peaceful relaxed atmosphere with lake and mountain views - smokefree.

Hulbert House 1888
Edward Sturt
Tel 03 4428767
68 Ballarat Street,
Queenstown
Fax 03 4428767

Single: $150
Double/twin: $180-200
Breakfast: Cooked
Beds: 3Q 3S
Evening meal: Not available
Bathrooms: 3EN 1PR

Hulbert House, a Victorian Villa of 17 rooms, has provided Old World hospitality for over a century. Its historic importance is protected by Covenant, and it offers unique Bed and Breakfast accommodation to the quality standards of the Heritage Inns of New Zealand. It's setting in an English-style garden with magnificent views of lake and mountains creates a private and peaceful haven just four minutes walk from the town centre.

Monaghan Homestay
Elsie and Pat Monaghan **Double/twin:** $90
Tel: 03 4428690
4 Panorama Terrace, Queenstown
Fax: 03 4428620

Ensuite, separate entrance. Close to town, great view.

Terrace View
Marjorie and Eddie Hutton **Double/twin:** $50-90
Tel: 03 4426751
8 MacKinnon Terrace, Sunshine Bay, Queenstown
Fax: 03 4426787

One twin, one king, one single - three rooms.

Turner Lodge
Hazel Seeto
Tel: 03 4429432
Cnr Turner St and Gorge Road,
Queenstown
Fax: 03 4429409

Single: $65
Double/twin: $100
Breakfast: Special
Beds: 1D 2S
Evening meal: Not available
Bathrooms: 2EN

The lodge is 3 minutes flat (no hills) walk to town. Off-street parking, laundry, ski/luggage storage, complimentary tea/coffee, full-menu breakfast, own TV.

Alexandra/Clyde
Thyme Lane - historic cottage

Leanne and Greg Holdsworth
Tel: 03 4492948
Earnscleugh Road, Alexandra
Fax: 03 4492947
Mob: 021 621007
Email: greg@holdsworths.co.nz

Single: $95
Double/twin: $125
Breakfast: Special
Beds: 1K
Evening meal: $45pp
Bathrooms: 1EN

Located in a quiet rural setting five minutes from Alexandra or Clyde this 130 year old rammed earth cottage has been restored with European flair while reflecting the historic gold mining past of this region. The cottage offers a bedroom with king size bed, ensuite and separate living/dining room. Every detail has been thought of in this romantic cottage; freshly roasted coffee, port, chocolates, fresh flowers, CDs and videos, hand painted fine linens and flowing fabrics. Breakfast is delivered in a basket for guests to retrieve at their leisure - an example would be poached fruits, local cheese and meats, home-made croissants, bagels and breads, home-made preserves, yogurt and cereals - with a selection of teas and fresh coffee. Candle-lit dinners are a specialty - your host, an ex-restaurateur prepares creative cuisine with local ingredients. Enquire about off-season discounts. Central Otago is the fastest growing wine-region in New Zealand and the gold-medal winning Black Ridge Vineyard is within staggering distance.

Clarke Homestay

Marion and John Clarke
Tel: 03 4487885
6 Rapuke Street
Alexandra

Single: $35
Double/twin: $60
Breakfast: Cooked
Beds: 1D 2S
Evening meal: $18pp
Bathrooms: 1GS

Enjoy Alexandra's unique scenery in our modern, sunny and warm home in a peaceful cul-de-sac. We are one hour from Queenstown, Wanaka and ski fields.

Dunstan House

William and Caroline Keely
Tel: 03 4492295
29 Sunderland Street
Clyde
Mob: 021 703123

Single: $90
Double/twin: $95-125
Breakfast: Special
Beds: 3Q 1S
Evening meal: Restaurant
Bathrooms: 3EN 1GS

Historic stone building in main street of Clyde - built in 1900 recently restored. In-house restaurant specialising in regional food and wines.

Freshfields

Robbie Wyatt   Lyn Somerville
Tel: 03 4492915
Rapid 489, Waikerikeri Valley
Alexandra
Fax: 03 4492916

Single: $50
Double/twin: $60
Breakfast: Continental
Beds: 1D 3S
Evening meal: Not available
Bathrooms: 1PR

Enjoy the peace, privacy, and non-smoking environment of our country acre. Be comfortable in our self-contained cottage. Handy to walks, wineries and lots more.

Iversen

Robyn and Roger Marshall
Tel: 03 4492520
47 Blackman Road, Earnscleugh,
Alexandra
Fax: 03 4492519

Single: $45
Double/twin: $80
Breakfast: Continental
Beds: 2Q
Evening meal: $25pp
Bathrooms: 1GS

Our specially built detatched accommodation allows you to enjoy privacy or share time with us. Relax in our quiet garden/orchard setting and walk in the adjoining hills.

Riverside B&B

Barbara Carter
Tel: 03 4485385
2 Bringham St, Alexandra
Mob: 021 662762

Double/twin: $90

Olde world charm close to shops and river.

Roxburgh

Norvalea Orchard

Richard and Wendy Turner
Tel: 03 4466714
Dalmuir Road, Ettrick, Roxburgh
Fax: 03 4466724
Free: 0800 226308

Double/twin: $60-80

Farmstay on homely kiwi family orchard. Picturesque setting.

Garston
Mataura Valley Station Farmstay Fishing Lodge

Robyn and David Parker
Tel: 03 2488552
Cainard Road, Garston
Queenstown - Te Anau Highway
Fax: 03 2488552

Single: $50-60
Double/twin: $100-110
Breakfast: Special
Beds: 2D 4S
Evening meal: $20pp
Bathrooms: 2EN 2FS

Welcome to our 19,000 acre high country sheep and cattle station, overlooking the Mataura river. Comfortable, modern home with glorious views and all day sunshine. Experience Alpine tranquility 10kms from the Queenstown-Te Anau highway. Fresh organic, farm-style meals, 4 wheel drive tours, fishing guides and aerial trips by arrangement. Relax and enjoy the scenery, take an apline walk, participate in farming activities, catch a brown trout, play in the river, count the sheep (approximately 10,000) or the 250 cattle. Paradise ducks nest on the creek, sky harks trill and hawks soar. A NZ falcon may rest on the rooftop. A great base for travel to Queenstown or Fiordland. We aim to make your stay a special memory.
Enjoy a real NZ high country experience.
We look forward to meeting you.

Te Anau
Cosy Kiwi

Virginia and Gerhard Hirner
Tel: 03 2497475
186 Milford Road, Te Anau
Fax: 03 2498471
Free: 0800 249700
Email: cosykiwi@teanau.co.nz

Single: $50-60
Double/twin: $75-95
Breakfast: Special
Beds: 3K 4Q 7S
Evening meal: Not available
Bathrooms: 6EN

Virginia and Gerhard and our 2 children welcome you to our all NEW Bed & Breakfast House. (We both have worked in Hospitality for over 20 years, we can speak German) We are located on the main road towards Milford Sound, close to the police-station, only 3 minutes walk to town centre, shops, restaurants and other amenities. All rooms come with ensuite, TV and new décor, double glazed windows for warmth and sound proofing. (Paraplegic room is available) We offer you off-street parking, safe storage, laundry, telephone, fax, dining-room/loungeroom with coffee making facilities, outdoor BBQ and an upstairs terrace with sun loungers overlooking our beautiful mountain ranges. All excursion trips can be booked with us, with bus pick-up at the gate. Our breakfast buffet will be served in our dining room with lots of homemade breads, jams, preserves, yoghurt and pancakes.
Directions: Main road to Milford Sound opposite school on right, just look for our sign 'Cosy Kiwi'. Inspection welcome. (Introductory offer receive a free gift.)
Note: Family room also available (sleeps 5) $110-145.

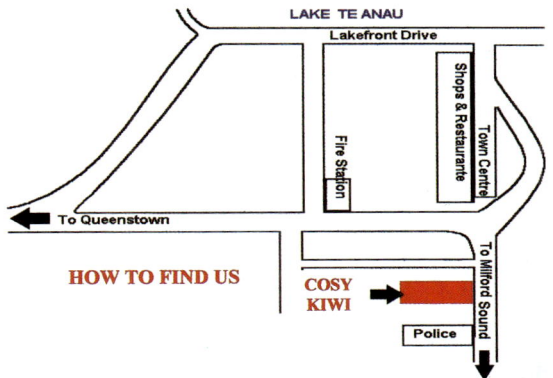

Joans Bed & Breakfast

Joan Kirtlan
Tel: 03 2497712
58 Mokonui Street
Te Anau

Single: $40
Double/twin: $70
Breakfast: Cooked
Beds: 1D 2S
Evening meal: Not available
Bathrooms: 1GS

Joan invites you to spend some time at her Mokonui Street modern home. Splendid views of mountains. Interests are conservation, organic gardening, patchwork, embroidery and family.

Rose 'n' Reel Farmstay

Lyn and Lex Lawrence
Tel: 03 2497582
Ben Loch Lane, Te Anau
Fax: 03 2497582
Mob: 025 545723

Double/twin: $75

Quality accommodation with magic lake and mountain views.

Shakespeare House

Jeff and Margaret Henderson
Tel: 03 2497349
10 Dusky Street, Te Anau
Southland
Fax: 03 2497629

Double/twin: $98

Family unit - Laundry - cooked breakfast - ensuites - king beds.

Manapouri

The Cottage

Don and Joy MacDuff
Tel: 03 2496838
Waiau Street
Manapouri
Fax: 03 2496839

Single: $55
Double/twin: $75
Breakfast: Continental
Beds: 1Q 1D 1S
Evening meal: $25pp
Bathrooms: 2EN

Our cottage home is welcoming and tranquil. Surrounded by trees, views of river and mountains, cottage garden, two minute walk to where boats depart for Doubtful Sound. Cooked breakfast avail extra $5pp. www.fiordland.org.nz/html/cottage.html